MYSTERIOUS STORIES
FROM THE BIBLE

1

RUTH REDDING BRAND
CHARLES MILLS

REVIEW AND HERALD® PUBLISHING ASSOCIATION
HAGERSTOWN, MD 21740

This book was
Edited by Gerald Wheeler
Designed by Patricia S. Wegh
Cover design by Ron J. Pride
Cover illustration by Kim Justinen
Typeset: 12/14 Stone Informal

PRINTED IN U.S.A.

99 98   10 9 8 7 6 5 4 3 2

R&H Cataloging Service
Brand, Ruth Redding
     Mysterious stories from the Bible, by Ruth
Redding Brand and Charles Mills.

     1. Bible stories.   I. Mills, Charles Henning.
1950-   II. Title.
                    220.9505

ISBN 0-8280-0709-8

① The Three Visitors

Stacey lifted a finger to her lips and frowned. "Be quiet!" she whispered. "Do you want us to get caught?"

Her two friends shook their heads slowly from side to side and peered into the leafy shadows beyond the dense row of bushes. "Maybe we should just go back into town and forget the whole thing," Jason stammered, his voice nowhere near its usual, slow-paced calm. "I mean, what if old man Appleby's not in his house and is out wandering around, looking for kids like us trying to sneak onto his property?"

First Stacey glanced over at the dark-skinned boy, then at the silent fourth grader crouching beside her. "You guys aren't scared, are you?"

"Of course not!" Maria laughed, lifting her chin slightly. "Didn't I dare you to bring us here in the first place?" She brushed stray strands of shiny black hair from her forehead and cleared her throat. "Besides, I'm not worried at all. He's just an old man who lives in a big house by the river."

"Yeah," Jason whispered. "And he's also an old man who never goes into town. He just stays out here and waits for those trucks to come. One drove by here about 15 minutes ago, remember?" The boy paused. "Haven't you ever wondered what's in the wooden boxes they deliver? My dad says old man Appleby's probably building an airplane or boat or something. But I think he's making coffins. Or maybe even a scaffold to hang people on."

Maria groaned. "He's not doing any such thing. You've got a weird imagination. I'll bet he's just adding on a room, like my neighbor did last summer. Lots of trucks came to his house too."

"But haven't you seen the addresses and strange writing on those boxes?" Jason pressed. "I'll bet your neighbor didn't get his building supplies from places like Turkey or Jordan or Egypt. Last week I peeked into one of those trucks. The driver was getting a soft drink at the gas station, so I jumped up and looked inside." The boy shook his head. "No, sir. Old man Appleby isn't building a playroom or putting together a boat. He's up to something, something creepy, and it's our duty to find out what it is."

Stacey shrugged. "So, let's get goin'. We haven't got all day, you know." The girl pointed down the long, tree-shrouded pathway leading from the main road into the heart of the property. "We're not going to find out anything squatting here in these bushes like a bunch of scared rabbits. You dared me to go, and I agreed to lead this expedition. Now *come on!*"

The 10-year-old swept her hand in a quick arch over her head and began creeping forward, followed by her two reluctant comrades. Elm branches, disturbed by the gentle autumn breezes, creaked overhead, and somewhere an unseen crow called out a warning. But this time nothing was going to stop them from discovering for themselves what lay in the old house surrounded by dark trees.

Silently, they slipped through the shadows until the trees hid the trio from view, leaving only the moan of the wind and the cry of the distant crow to disturb the afternoon peace.

After what seemed like hours Stacey's hand shot up. "There. See it? That's the house."

Maria and Jason blinked as their mouths dropped open. Before them, resting at the edge of a small clearing, sat a tall, stately mansion. Brown creeping vines and odd-shaped branches held the structure tightly to the earth as if afraid it would try to escape.

"That house must be a million years old," Jason breathed. "Probably as old as Appleby himself."

"Nobody lives that long," Maria chided.

As Stacey led the others forward, she said quietly, "My mom said the mansion has been here since she was a little girl. It was old even then. No one comes back here now, except those trucks. Even they don't stay long."

The three crept up the front steps. Dead leaves lay in piles across the broad porch and fluttered dryly in the breeze.

Slowly, carefully, they edged to the dust-smudged windows and peered in. "Do you see anything?" Jason asked, his words shaking just a little.

Maria stared for a moment. "There's something over there by the far wall. It looks like a box or maybe a . . . a . . ."

"Coffin," the boy interrupted. "That's what it is. It's a big coffin the old man puts dead people in right before he buries them down by the river." Jason straightened, trying to support himself on wobbly legs. "And I'm not gonna stick around for the funeral. I'm gettin' outta here!"

He turned to run, but found himself face-to-face with a man standing at the top of the porch steps. Deep-blue eyes stared at him out of a tanned and wrinkled face. The old man's excited voice broke the stillness.

"Did you see it? Did you see it? The truck left it just minutes ago." He paused. "Or was that the one that came yesterday? No. No. Couldn't be. Rained yesterday. Trucks don't come in the rain. Too much mud, you know. Had to be the day before."

Jason backed up slowly, his mouth suddenly dry. "N . . . no, sir. We didn't see anything. Honest."

The old man started toward them, limping slightly, occasionally leaning on a crooked cane. "Why, it's just inside the door. You can't miss it." He stopped and pointed at Jason. "Who are you?"

The boy cleared his throat as he felt himself press up against the front door of the ancient mansion. "I'm J-J-Jason."

"Of course you are. You look like a Jason. If your name were Billy or Fred, it would be all wrong. You're Jason, and that's that."

"Th-thank you, sir."

The man turned to the others. "And who might you . . . wait . . . I know you." He pointed at the girl with the blond hair and rosy cheeks standing silently by the window. "You're Stacey."

Maria and Jason's eyes widened. "How'd he know your name?" they asked the girl.

She shrugged. "Lucky guess?"

"Whatta ya mean, lucky guess?" the old man chuckled. "Why, I've known—"

"If you're so smart, what's her name?" Stacey interrupted, pointing at Maria beside her.

The man paused, studying Stacey, then nodded slowly. "I see," he said softly. "Now I understand."

Stacey let her gaze drop from the man's eyes. "Go ahead," she urged, her words not much above a whisper. "See if you can guess what her name is too."

Maria smiled shyly up at the stranger. "You don't have to," she announced. "I'll tell you. It's Maria, and I'm from Mexico. Have you ever been to Mexico?"

The old man rubbed his whiskered chin thoughtfully. "Hmm, let's see. Yes. During the big war. Went through Mexico on my way to the Panama Canal. Had to make sure the Japanese didn't blow it up. That would have been a real mess. They didn't, so I went to Europe."

"You were in Europe?" Jason asked, not wanting to be left out of the conversation. The old man no longer seemed anywhere near as scary as the boy had imagined he'd be.

"Traveled all over the world. Europe, Africa, Asia. Even went to a really dangerous place once."

"Where?" the young boy asked.

"California," the man announced, then burst out laughing. "'Bout got run over by a sports car. Everybody drives sports cars in California." His laughter lifted the fear from the old mansion and replaced it with a kind of homeyness.

The children found themselves smiling in spite of themselves. No one could laugh this hard and happily and be dangerous at the same time.

The man suddenly stopped and lifted a finger. "Wait. The box! You must see what's in it before you go."

Jason's chuckle froze on his face. *Oh yes. The coffin.*

Maria stepped forward and pointed at her young companion. "Jason thinks there's something dead in it."

"He's right," the old man nodded. "What's in there is very, very dead."

The girl's eyes widened again. "Oh . . . I don't want to see it. We really must be going now."

The old man ignored her and hurried through the door. "My sister sent it. She's always sending me things." The children watched through the window as he sprinted to the big rectangular box at the far end of the spacious living room. The man's voice echoed through unseen corridors as he spoke.

"Government said it was OK, although they couldn't for the life of them figure out why she'd want to ship something so odd and useless out of the country."

"Government?" Jason called from the doorway.

"That's right. Lebanon. You know, the Middle Eastern country at the eastern end of the Mediterranean Sea." Gnarled hands removed the metal bands encircling the box. "Guess no one had ever made such an odd request before."

By now he had the top of the container creaking open. Maria covered her eyes with her hands and pressed her face against Stacey's shoulder. "I don't want to see a dead person," she wailed.

"What?" the old man spun around. "Dead person? Where?"

Jason pointed. "In the box."

The old man jumped back, holding his chest. "Mercy me! You say there's a dead person in there? Well, I sure got the wrong shipment if there is."

Maria peeked between her fingers. "You . . . you mean there isn't a dead person in there?"

The man tilted his head. "Now, why would I put a dead person in my living room? It's untidy enough as it is without a corpse lying around." He reached into the box. "There's nothing in here but an old dead tree limb." A tangled collection of branches emerged from the top of the container. "This is from a cedar tree—you know, cedars of Lebanon? It's all in the Bible."

Jason let out a long sigh. "A tree limb? Why would your sister send you that?"

"Oh, she's always shipping stuff off to me. House is full up to the eaves with strange, mysterious trinkets—some very old, some new." The man set the large limb down on the floor, then began rummaging through the carton as if looking for something. "I hope she didn't forget. Don't want to miss it."

Maria blinked. "Miss what? Was she supposed to send you something else in that box?"

"Of course, of course," the old man answered, leaning far into the dark confines of the container. "Wouldn't be like her to forget." He straightened, clutching a small package in his right hand. "There, see? She remembered. Always includes a tape."

By now the old man's fascinating antics had drawn the children into the large living room. They stood by the front door, their curiosity stronger than their fear.

Jason lifted his hand shyly. "What's on the tape?"

The old man stopped. "What tape?"

"The one in your hand."

"Oh, I haven't listened to it yet. Can't tell you. But if you'll give me a moment, I'll get my machine. Can't listen without a machine, you know."

"I guess not," Jason said, an unexpected smile playing at the sides of his mouth. Mr. Appleby was certainly an interesting character. An old mansion, hidden deep in a forest, filled with things gathered from around the world, was enough to make any boy or girl tingle with excitement, now that no dead bodies were lying around.

"Here we go," the man called out triumphantly from inside a tall closet out in the entryway. "My cassette player." He motioned for his young visitors to gather around as he seated himself on the cloth-covered couch. "Make yourselves comfortable," he encouraged. "My sister's writing a book for kids . . . hey, you're kids . . . this is terrific. You'll be the first to hear her stories."

"Stories?" Maria questioned, settling herself on a dusty beanbag under the window. "What kind of stories?"

"Bible kind," the old man announced, slipping the cassette tape into his battered recorder. "She travels around the Middle East—the Holy Lands—where people are digging up things from Bible times. Then she tells these stories based on what the Bible says and what she's uncovered. I've got a whole collection of these tapes. Get new ones every shipment."

With a click the recorder lid fell into place, and the old man looked up and grinned. "Now, you three keep still and listen. Ready?"

"Ready!" Stacey, Jason, and Maria sang out.

Mr. Appleby pressed the play button with his index finger. At first the children heard only the sounds of crickets and a distant dog barking. Then a woman's voice, clear and determined, filled the shadowy room.

✗ ✗ ✗

Abram leaned against the tent pole at the opening of his tent, dreaming in the sunshine.

"Ab-ra-ham . . . Ab-ra-ham . . ." He said the word slowly, tasting it on his tongue.

"No longer will you be called Abram, but Abraham," God had told him. "And Sarai will now be known as Sarah."

Abraham smiled. He had liked his name Abram. It had

meant that the father is exalted. But the name Abraham announced that he would be the father of multitudes. Was this, he wondered, God's way of telling him once more that the land of Canaan would belong to his children?

And Sarai . . . her name meant "princess." "Sarah," as the Canaanites pronounced it, still had the same meaning. Did it suggest that she was fit to be the mother of kings?

Suddenly he heard a step and sat up straight. There, a little way off, stood three strangers. To pause before someone's tent was just the same as knocking at the door. Quickly Abraham ran to them, bowing as he went.

"Please, gentlemen, do not think of continuing on your journey without stopping here to rest awhile," he said. "Won't you sit in the shade while I bring some water to wash your feet and fix you a bite of food? You have honored me by coming to my home, so do let me serve you."

The strangers flashed happy smiles at Abraham. "We're glad to accept your invitation," they replied.

Then Abraham got busy. He rushed into the tent and called, "Sarah, Sarah, we have company! Get out some of your best flour and make some bread for our guests."

Whirling around to find a servant, Abraham directed, "Quick! Get some water for our guests." The servant sprang into action. He grabbed the water jug and splashed water from it into clay basins. Then he ran to the strangers, carrying one basin at a time, the water sloshing on his toes as he went.

The strangers again smiled as they took off their sandals and eased their hot, dusty feet into the cool water.

In the meantime, Abraham had hurried to the nearby pasture where his cattle grazed. In a pen made of rocks stood a long-eared calf and its mother. *It is good that I still have my best and fattest calf for visitors*, Abraham thought as he jumped over the rough stone wall and chased the calf around the pen.

Other people in Abraham's household stared as he finally wrapped his long arms around the calf and gave it to a servant to butcher. "There must be someone special visiting," they told one another, wagging their heads wisely. "Abraham is going to kill the fatted calf instead of a baby goat."

Rushing back to the tent, he called, "Sarah, how is the bread coming?"

Her eyes twinkled as she rubbed her nose with the back of one flour-coated hand, then pointed to the oven. The clay oven, shimmering with the heat of the fire burning inside, was covered with flat, round bread, made from Sarah's finest wheat. Abraham flashed her a grateful smile and ran back to prepare the calf.

Hastily cutting it into pieces that would cook quickly, he threaded the meat on wooden skewers and held them over a fire.

At last the meal was ready. Abraham invited his three

visitors to sit on mats under the shade of a big terebinth tree. The visitors sat cross-legged, their now-clean feet not dirtying their clothes. Abraham stood politely while Sarah, just as politely, hid behind the tent flap, peeking out and listening.

"This is just a bite to keep you going," Abraham remarked in an offhand way. "No trouble at all, of course."

Sarah grinned. It was the custom always to treat guests like royalty and pretend it was nothing at all, but it still amused her.

Abraham smiled with satisfaction as he saw his guests enjoy the meal. Wrapping the flat bread around the meat, they popped it in their mouths, then tipped their heads back and drank deep swallows of goat's milk.

"Won't you have more?" Abraham urged. "Here, do have some curds with your bread." The strangers dipped into the tangy, white milk curds.

When Abraham could not convince the strangers to eat any more, they turned to him and asked, "Where is your wife, Sarah?"

Listening behind the tent flap, she sucked in her breath. What kind of men were these? Only those who knew her very, very well would dare ask such a question. And she had never seen them before in her life.

After only the briefest pause, Abraham answered, "She is in the tent."

Then one of the men looked Abraham straight in the eye and said firmly, "I will come back at this time next year, and when I do, your wife, Sarah, will have a son."

Sarah gasped, then clapped her hand over her mouth to muffle her sudden laughter. These men could not know her so well after all! Imagine telling her husband, nearly 100 years old, that his wife, almost 90, would have a baby! What a joke! She'd been through all that kind of false hope too many times before to believe that now in her old age she would have a child.

But the stranger continued speaking to Abraham. "Why

did Sarah laugh and say, 'I am too old to have a child'?" he asked. "Is anything too hard for the Lord?"

Sarah's face began to flush while her hands suddenly felt cold. This must be the Lord Himself who was speaking. And she had laughed! Hardly knowing what she was doing, she burst out of the tent and cried, "I didn't laugh!"

The Stranger looked at her kindly but seriously. "Yes, you did," He answered gently.

Sarah turned away, tears blinding her eyes. Shame, hope, excitement, a new trust in God—all filled her heart. The strangers, messengers from heaven, had come right to her tent and told her and Abraham that she would have a son. One of them had read her every thought, and if He could do that, could He not work a miracle in her old body and at last give her that longed-for son? Tears streamed down her face as she remembered the question, "Is anything too hard for the Lord?"

"No, Lord, it isn't," she whispered.

Abraham's special visitors got up to leave. Still a polite host, Abraham walked with them until they came to a high hill. Far below they could see the Salt Sea sparkling in the sunlight, and the green valley dotted with its five cities of the plain.

Two of the visitors thanked Abraham for his hospitality and continued their journey toward the city of Sodom. The Other stayed behind to talk with him.

"I have another purpose for my visit," the heavenly Stranger said to Abraham. "The sins of Sodom and Gomorrah shout all the way to heaven. I am here to judge their cities."

Abraham's face turned white. He thought of his nephew Lot, who lived in Sodom. In spite of some failings in the past, Lot still worshiped the God of heaven. Because the wickedness of Sodom and Gomorrah was so great, Abraham knew God would have to destroy the cities. But what about Lot and his family? Wouldn't they too be destroyed? And what of other people who worshiped God? Surely there must be some!

Bowing before the heavenly Stranger, he asked, "Will You destroy the righteous with the wicked? Suppose there are 50 righteous people in the city of Sodom. Surely You would not destroy it if there are 50 righteous people in it, would You?"

The Lord looked into Abraham's troubled eyes. "No, Abraham, I will not destroy it if I find 50 righteous people."

Abraham took a deep breath. "But Lord, suppose there are only 45 righteous people there. For just five less than 50, You would not wipe it out, would You?

"No, Abraham, I would not."

The patriarch was not ready to give up yet. "I know I'm not worthy to ask, Lord, but what if there were only 40 righteous people in the city?"

"For the sake of 40 people I would spare the city."

"Oh, please don't be angry with me," Abraham persisted, "but suppose you found only 30 righteous people."

"If I find 30 righteous people, I will not touch the city," the Lord assured him.

Abraham paused, and worked the toe of his sandal back and forth in the dust. Did he dare ask for more?

"Lord," he urged, "forgive me, but suppose You find only 20 righteous people in the city. Would you wipe it out then?"

The Lord placed a hand on Abraham's shoulder. "If I find 20 righteous people, I will spare it," He promised.

Surely, Abraham thought, *in the whole city of Sodom there must be 20 righteous people!* He knew of four in Lot's family, but surely there had to be others! But he would not ask the Lord to spare the city just for his four relatives.

"Lord, do not be angry with me, and I will ask no more. But what if there were only 10?"

And the Lord assured him, "Yes, Abraham, my friend, for the sake of 10 righteous people I will pass it by."

That night Sarah sang and her eyes danced as she

walked with Abraham beneath the stars. She would have a son, for nothing is too hard for the Lord!

But Abraham kept asking himself, *Are there 10 righteous people in Sodom? Are there?*

✕ ✕ ✕

The tape ended. Mr. Appleby reached down and pressed the stop button. With a click the room fell silent.

The three children sat motionless, listening to the last words the woman had spoken echoing softly through the rafters overhead.

Stacey glanced over at the man and nodded. "I like that story," she said.

The old man smiled sadly. "I once knew a little girl who loved to hear Bible stories. Her mom said she'd listen for hours if someone would tell them to her."

"Well, I'll listen," Maria announced.

"Me too," Jason added, "if they're as neat as that one. You say you have more tapes?"

"Lots of 'em," the man nodded. "That is, if I can remember where I put them." He bent and looked out the window. "You kids had better get back into town. Sun's almost down. Gets kinda dark out here at night." Standing stiffly, he fumbled for his cane. "Come, I'll walk you to the main road."

After a few minutes of rummaging through the closet, Mr. Appleby emerged with a flashlight held tightly in one hand. The children followed him out onto the porch and descended the stairs. Happily they trudged after their newfound friend along the darkening pathway leading through the trees and out to the bushes guarding the Appleby property.

"Do come again," the old man urged once as they paused in the dim light under the lamppost by the road. "I enjoy talking to young folk like you. Sorta reminds me of years gone by. I used to be a teacher, you know—a professor."

"Professor Appleby," Jason said softly, "may we come

back tomorrow after school?"

"Sure!" Then the man paused and turned to face Stacey. "I like to make new friends. Sometimes I get a little lonely in that mansion all by myself. But be sure you get your parents' permission, now."

The girl with the blond hair studied her toes. "I'll come too, if that's OK. Maria and I want to hear all the stories."

"Good," Professor Appleby said with a wrinkled smile. "Then we'll listen to more tapes, and I'll show you wonderful things from faraway places. We'll have lots of fun discovering what that globe-trotting sister of mine has been digging up."

He turned and disappeared down the winding path, leaving three tired and happy children behind.

The trio waved goodbye and headed toward town along the well-lit road. Stacey was strangely silent, but Jason and Maria spoke of nothing but angels and surprise visitors.

Tomorrow they'd hear more. Tomorrow they'd sit once again and listen to Professor Appleby's sister tell another story about a distant land and people who lived a long, long time ago.

②

Destruction of Sodom

Hey, Professor Appleby, what are you doing up in that tree?" The three children stood at the base of a towering oak, staring up into its branches. They'd come to hear more stories but instead found their new friend hanging upside-down high above the tall grasses and tangled weeds surrounding the old mansion.

"Oh. Hello there," the man called out. "Right on time, I see. You just go in and make yourselves comfortable, and I'll be down in a minute."

Stacey, Jason, and Maria shrugged and climbed the steps leading to the broad, leaf-covered porch. They were quickly learning that Professor Appleby was anything but your normal, run-of-the-mill person. If they found him hanging high in a tree, there must be a good explanation.

Snap! Crash!

The three turned just in time to see the old man land in the soft grasses at the base of the oak.

"Oh dear, oh dear!" Maria cried. "Professor Appleby has fallen out of the tree, and now he's dead."

"Hang on there, everybody," a muffled voice called from deep in the weeds. "I'm fit as a fiddle and ready to play, soon as I get this grass out of my mouth."

The children heard a lot of spitting and coughing, then a smiling face appeared above the rich carpet of woodland growth. "I got it. I got it! Can't say as I'm the best tree climber in the world, but I get the job done. See?"

The old man lifted his hand. In it he tightly gripped a collection of intertwined twigs and leaves.

"A nest," Jason said. "It's a bird's nest."

"Robin's nest," Professor Appleby said, stumbling to his feet and retrieving his cane. "Watched it built this spring.

Had four healthy little ones. They flew away about a month ago, so I figured I'd keep the nest in the house till next year. All winter long it'll remind me of their beautiful music and happy tweeting. It's my summer souvenir. Isn't it great?"

The children admired the carefully constructed nest in the old man's outstretched hand. "People need to remember the good things," he said. "Too many folk just concentrate on the bad. Must have both. Makes life balanced."

Maria giggled. "You didn't look too balanced out there on that limb."

Professor Appleby tilted back his head and laughed long and hard. "Right you are, my friend," he said, trying to catch his breath. "Now, there's something you can remember tomorrow, or the next day, or the one after that. Anytime you feel sad, just picture old man Appleby up in that tree, and it'll bring a smile to your face. I guarantee it."

Stacey stepped forward. "Are you OK? I mean, did the fall hurt you?"

The man smiled. "Oh, I'm fine, Stacey. Thanks for asking." He paused. "Any girl with the name of Stacey must be kind and thoughtful. All the Staceys I've ever known were like that."

The girl blushed just a little. "I . . . I . . ." Her words failed, and she pointed toward the house. "Do you have another tape to play for us today?"

"Sure do. It's a real gripper. Found it in the box under a pile of cedar cones. Picks up the story where yesterday's ended. Come on in, and I'll play it for you." He paused a second. "You did get permission from your parents to come, didn't you?"

They all nodded.

The group trudged into the high-ceilinged living room. "I straightened up a little," the old man said. "Gets a bit messy with just me bumping about in here. No need to clean. Don't get many visitors—that is, until you folks showed up."

Professor Appleby dug through a small box by the book-case until he found what he was looking for. "Here it is," he called triumphantly. "Didn't even lose it. Aren't you proud of me?"

The children nodded. "But where's the tape recorder?" Jason asked, eyeing the empty end table where the machine had rested the day before.

"Oh no," the Professor sighed. "Don't tell me I've misplaced it again." He looked around frantically. "Can't play a tape without a machine."

Then he paused and smiled. "Wait. I remember. I . . . put it . . . over here." He hurried to a shelf by the window. "No. I guess not."

Stacey rose and walked to a small bookcase standing by the couch. "How 'bout here?" she said, pushing aside a stack of dusty volumes.

Professor Appleby gasped. "Of course. There it is! That's where I keep it when it's not in the closet. How silly of me to forget."

Maria and Jason stared at Stacey for a long moment. "How'd you know?" they asked. "How'd you know where the tape recorder was?"

"Lucky guess," the girl shrugged. "Professor Appleby can figure out names—I can find tape recorders. No big deal."

The old man settled himself on the couch as the children gathered about. "Hold on to your hats," he called, sliding the cassette tape into position. This one's very exciting."

Pressing the play button, he waited. Soon the familiar sound of crickets filled the room as an unseen reader adjusted some papers. Then a rich female voice rattled the tiny speaker, and the story began.

✘ ✘ ✘

As the sun neared the western horizon and shadows began filling the plaza by the city gate, Lot scanned the milling crowd. Here, at the city gate, one could find all kinds of people. In the open area they conducted their business and traded news and gossip.

Lot liked being a part of the hustle and bustle of the city. He felt important when people came to him for advice. And they had done that ever since his uncle Abraham had rescued some citizens of Sodom from slavery.

But now as he watched the people, he noticed two men who were obviously strangers and newcomers. From their dusty feet and clothes he could tell that they had walked far.

Lot remembered how his uncle Abraham had always been kind to strangers. But the people of Sodom often treated visitors in shameful and cruel ways.

Jumping up, Lot ran to the two dusty men. "I, your servant, would be so pleased to have you in my home!" he told them. "Please come to my humble home where you can spend the night. In the morning you can be on your way."

"We wouldn't think of bothering you," the men answered. "We'll just wrap up in our robes right here by the gate."

But Lot insisted. "Oh, no, I can't allow you to do that. The people of this city are not always kind to visitors."

Finally the men agreed to go to his house, and he led them through the city streets to his fine home.

"Now," Lot said, when the men were inside, "my servants will draw water for your dusty feet while they bake bread for your supper."

The strangers quietly ate and drank as Lot watched them curiously. The two men seemed to have something serious on their minds, but they didn't talk about it.

Later as Lot and his servants rolled out mats for the men to sleep on, coarse, loud voices shattered the stillness.

"Hey, Lot!" a rough voice bellowed. Fists pounded on the door. "Send out your guests so we can have a little fun with them!"

Lot peeked out. Scores of men surrounded his house. Shouting, swearing, making crude jokes, the mob filled the street, demanding to see Lot's guests.

His face turned pale as he realized what kind of "fun" the wicked men wanted to have. They would probably leave the two strangers dead by morning if they got hold of them.

"Please stand back," he directed his guests as he squeezed out the door, quickly closing it behind him.

The men's voices grew louder as they saw Lot. "Where are they? Bring them out!"

"Have you so forgotten your manners that you would harm guests in our city?" Lot demanded. "Have you no shame at all? Stop and think what you're doing!"

But the men refused to listen. "Who do you think you are, anyway? You're nothing but a newcomer among us. Who made you a judge over us? Now, send out the men!"

"I can't do that!" Lot persisted, his face white as desert sand. "They are guests in my home. You know it is my duty to protect them. And it is your duty too!"

With a mighty roar the crowd pushed forward. "Don't talk to us about our duty!" someone shouted. "We want those men, and if you don't give them to us, we'll get you first."

"Come on, now," Lot begged, truly frightened. "Can't I offer you something else?"

"Stand back!" bawled a red-faced ape of a man as he tried to push past Lot. The heavy door creaked and splintered. Desperately Lot tried to get back into the house, but the men blocked his way.

Then Lot's guests decided things had gone far enough. With powerful arms they flung open the door and pulled Lot inside. Their eyes flashed with heavenly fire, and suddenly the wicked men of Sodom stumbled around in confusion. Strange lights danced before their eyes as objects seemed to lean toward them, then fell away. Lot's closed door refused to stay in one place. It appeared first on one side of the house, then the other. Cursing and moaning, the wicked men ran into each other as they vainly searched for the door to his house. Finally, unable to see, they crawled away on hands and knees.

Lot's eyes widened with wonder. Now he understood that the men were not men but angels. In fact, though Lot could not know it, they were the same angels who had visited Abraham earlier in the day.

The angels wasted no time now in telling him the purpose of their visit.

"Hurry, Lot, and warn your family that Sodom is about to be destroyed, for the Lord can no longer ignore its sins."

Quickly Lot gathered his family. His wife and their two daughters stood pale and shaking as he repeated the angels' words. Immediately the daughters began crying. "What about the men we plan to marry? They have to be warned. Oh, Father, please tell them!"

Out into the night he hurried. Past altars to Baal and drunken parties he hastened, until he came to the home of the young man engaged to one of his daughters.

Between breaths Lot gasped, "Two angels are at my house. They're going to destroy this city. Hurry! You must come with us to be saved!"

The young man threw back his head and laughed. "Are you serious?"

"It's true!" Lot insisted. "This city's wickedness has reached its end."

But the young man refused to listen. Shaking his head, he gently closed the door.

At the next house another young man opened the door, rubbing sleep from his eyes. "What are you doing here?" he yawned.

Quickly Lot repeated his message, but this one refused even to let him finish speaking.

"Destroy Sodom? You can't be serious! Now let me go back to sleep," he said. "Good night!"

"But—!" The door shut in Lot's face.

The sky had begun to lighten by the time Lot reached his own home. His daughters had only to look at his face to know he had failed to convince their young men to flee with them. His wife walked around and around her home, fingering her fine dishes, her costly jewelry, her rich tapestries and clothes. To Lot all this felt somehow unreal. All his wealth, everything he had, would soon be destroyed.

"It's time to go," the angels said.

Lot and his family lingered, but the angels grasped their hands and pulled them from the house. Half dragging them, the beings hurried them to the outskirts of the doomed city. "Now run for your lives!" the angels directed. "Run! Do not look back or stop anywhere. Run all the way to the mountains. If you don't, you'll be destroyed!"

"Oh, no, not the mountains!" Lot wailed. "Please! The mountains are so far away that we'd never make it before the destruction comes, and we're used to living in the city, and . . . How about letting us go to that little city over there?" Lot pointed with a shaky finger in the direction of a village later called Zoar—the Little One. "Oh, please let us go there!"

With amazing patience the angels listened to Lot's frantic plea. "All right," they assured him, "we will spare that city from destruction. But hurry, for we cannot do anything until you are safely there!"

Lot and his family rushed toward the cluster of houses. Suddenly, just as they reached the little city, the sky lit up with a brightness that made the noonday sun look dim. A red glow spread above them, around them. But Lot and his daughters remembered the angel's words—"Don't look back."

His wife, stumbling along after her family, dropped farther and farther back. Behind her were her friends, her home, all the things that made life pleasant. She *must* look one more time at Sodom!

Quickly, yearningly, she turned just for one last glimpse. Instantly her body became a pillar of salt. Had she been able to see, a fearful sight would have met her astonished eyes. Fire roared through the valley and rained from the sky. The wicked cities of Sodom and Gomorrah, and the other cities in the valley, crackled and burned and smoked. Sulphurous gases exploded and the ever-present tar pits blazed with deadly heat. Burning with the justice of a God who could no longer bear to see people destroy themselves in slow and painful ways, the cities blazed into a thick layer of ashes.

The next morning Abraham hurried to a high hill overlooking the valley where Sodom, Gomorrah, and the other cities had been. Blackened earth and dense smoke answered his nagging question, Had there been 10 righteous people in Sodom?

No, not even 10.

⚔ ⚔ ⚔

Professor Appleby and the children sat in silence trying to imagine the horror Abraham felt as he looked down into the valley where Lot and his family had lived.

Finally Professor Appleby stretched his legs and arms. "Tomorrow, if you stop by I'll play you some stories about a young boy sold into slavery who then became a great ruler in a foreign land. My sister recorded them in Egypt where he lived. Will you come back?"

"Of course!" the three children shouted. Maria stood to leave. "I want to hear them all. Your sister sounds nice."

Professor Appleby nodded. "Oh yes," he said. "She's wonderful."

At the front door the children paused. "What's her name?" Jason asked.

The old man lifted his chin proudly and spoke with loving reverence. "Her name is Margaret Brewster. But I just call her Maggie B. You can call her that too, if you want."

"Maggie B," Jason repeated. "That's a nice name."

The children walked out into the late-afternoon sunshine and down the green carpeted path leading to the road. Professor Appleby stood on the porch waving.

"See you tomorrow," he called.

The forest swallowed up the children as the wind brushed the face of the old mansion. The man turned. "Now, where did I leave that broom and dustpan?" he mumbled to himself. "Have to tidy up a bit more. My special guests will be returning."

Humming a nameless tune, he closed the door and disappeared into the shadows.

③

Potiphar, Prison, and Pharoah

Acool autumn rain fell as the children arrived at the mansion the next afternoon. Professor Appleby waited for them on the porch.

"Welcome, welcome," he called out when he saw his three new friends splashing through the puddles by the pathway as they hurried out of the forest and into the clearing. "I'm sure glad your parents don't mind you visiting an old man. Come in quickly. I have something to show you."

Stacey, Maria, and Jason ran the remaining distance and were soon warming their wet faces by a crackling fire in the den. It was a room they hadn't seen before. Colorful flags and intricate tapestries from countries with strange-sounding names covered the walls. Professor Appleby spoke with a quiet excitement as he showcased each item.

"This rug is from Persia," he said, fingering the thick, boldly detailed material. Maggie B found it in a little shop outside Isfahan when she was researching the story of Esther.

"And here's a prayer rug from Turkey. Notice how carefully the artist has woven red and green threads to make this lovely design. When the muezzin—that's the fellow who climbs up in his tower and calls everyone to prayer—begins his five-times-a-day chant, faithful Muslims roll out their prayer rugs. They all turn toward the holy city of Mecca and bow low to the ground."

Professor Appleby leaned back and cupped his hands around his mouth. In a voice haunting and full he sang out, "*La . . . ilaha . . . illa . . . llah!*" The sound echoed through the dark corridors of the old mansion.

When the last note had faded, he turned to the children and smiled broadly. "That means 'There is no god but

God.' Isn't it beautiful?"

The children nodded enthusiastically. Somehow, in this ancient building tucked away in a dark forest, in a room surrounded by colorful tapestries from distant countries, the lilting chant seemed to belong, to be a part of the mystery of the professor's life, and that of his wandering sister.

"But that's not what I wanted to show you," the old man announced. "Come over here." He motioned for them to follow.

The professor paused by a little container resting on the windowsill. "Look in there and tell me what you see," he invited.

Jason leaned forward and peered into the jar. "I see a bunch of seeds," he said. "Are those magic or something?"

"No, no," the old man laughed. "There are no magic seeds. But those are very, very special. You see, those are wheat seeds from a land called Egypt. They reminded my sister of an exciting story from the Bible as she was exploring along the majestic Nile River. Why don't we sit down over here and listen to what she had to say?"

The group made themselves comfortable by the warm fireplace while Professor Appleby adjusted his tape recorder. This time, when he pressed the play button, they heard no crickets chirping. Instead, the children heard the soft splash of water and the creak and thump of a wooden boat. The professor's sister was sailing up the Nile with a hot summer sun shining overhead. It didn't take long before the children realized they were in for a most exciting visit with the unseen Maggie B.

✕ ✕ ✕

A miserable group of people, men, women, and children huddled together under the hot Egyptian sun, waiting to be sold to the highest bidder. Joseph was next.

The Ishmaelite traders eagerly pushed him forward.

Joseph looked into the crowd of bored faces and prayed

that he would not show the fear he felt.

"Ah, we've got a real prize here!" the auctioneer shouted, pointing to Joseph. "This one's young enough to learn, but old enough to work hard. And he even looks intelligent."

A roar of boisterous laughter greeted his words, and the bidding began.

On the far edge of the crowd stood a man with an air of authority. Quietly he signaled to a bidder near the front of the crowd. Joseph saw the distant man lift his hand, palm up. From watching other sales, Joseph knew what that meant—no limit. "I'll pay whatever I have to, but I'll buy him."

Joseph soon learned that the man who bought him was Potiphar, captain of the palace guard. Although Potiphar spoke in the strange Egyptian language, as Joseph listened and watched carefully he understood that his new master

wanted to know his name. Pointing to himself, he said clearly, "Joseph."

"Ah, Yosef," Potiphar repeated.

Joseph marveled at Potiphar's mud-brick house with its many rooms and a staircase to the second floor, its walls surrounding a courtyard with a reflecting pool, furniture to sleep in and sit on unlike anything he had known in Canaan. He listened carefully to everything anyone said, and soon began to understand the Egyptian language.

Potiphar assigned Joseph to work in his bakery. Soon the new slave mastered each task. He carried grain, had it ground into flour, and baked all the many different breads and pastries known to the Egyptians.

Potiphar's servant in charge of the bakery had trouble keeping measurements straight, so Joseph helped him. When new slaves arrived at the bakery, Joseph taught them all he knew and organized their work.

Before long Potiphar heard what a good worker Joseph was.

"I could use someone like that to handle my household accounts and keep everything running smoothly," he said to himself. "I'll put him on trial first, though."

Joseph liked working in Potiphar's large, beautiful home. But at night he thought about his own home, and his father Jacob, and a lump of loneliness formed in his throat. Then he would look at the stars peeking in through the small windows at the top of the wall of his room and think, *Those same stars shine over my father's tent. And the same God watches over each of us.*

One day Potiphar declared, "From now on you will supervise my household staff and all my business. You're the best manager I've ever seen and had."

Joseph worked hard to keep Potiphar's trust. But one person made his job difficult. And that was Potiphar's wife.

Day after day she tried to get him to pay attention to her instead of doing his job. She even tried to persuade

Joseph to love her as her husband did.

"Come on, Joseph," she said one day. "No one is around to see what we do. What are you afraid of?"

"Mistress of the house," Joseph answered respectfully but firmly, "my master trusts me. He has put me in charge of his whole house and treated me kindly. Your husband has given me the right to everything except one thing, and that, of course, is you. You are his wife, not mine. How could I break his trust and sin against my God?"

But she paid no attention to his words. Giggling softly, she grabbed his clothes. Joseph pulled away from her and ran out the door, leaving his garment in her hands.

Now she was angry—and scared. What if someone had seen him racing out of the house? What would they think about her? She began to scream.

Servants came running from everywhere—all except Joseph, of course. "What's wrong?" they asked.

"Get my husband! Get my husband!" she screamed.

When Potiphar arrived, she threw herself at him, sobbing and wailing.

"That Hebrew slave—he—he attacked me! See? When I screamed he fled in such a hurry that he left his garment here!" Her eyes rolled wildly and she sobbed loudly, but Potiphar noticed that no tears fell.

Inwardly he groaned. He didn't believe for a minute that Joseph had done anything wrong, but he certainly could not call his wife a liar in front of all the servants. What a dilemma! If Joseph had really tried to hurt her, he must die. But he knew his slave was innocent.

Turning to his guards, his face white with anger, he directed, "Throw Yosef in prison!"

There! He'd done it, and lost the best business manager that he'd ever had.

The prison fortress in which Joseph found himself offered no light or comfort, only gloomy rooms crowded with prisoners. With the other prisoners he worked under the watchful eye and ready whip of an overseer, carrying mud and straw to make bricks. At night he slumped to the hard dirt floor, grateful for rest among the fleas, lice, and mosquitoes.

Canaan seemed far away and long ago. Had he really been the pampered son of an important man? Had he once worn a beautiful coat instead of a filthy rag?

But as Joseph listened to the groans of the men around him, his heart softened. Some of them had committed crimes and deserved punishment. But some, he felt sure, were as innocent as he.

Little by little Joseph made friends with the prisoners. Day by day they learned to trust him with their problems. Of all the prisoners, only Joseph approached the guards to ask for mercy for others, not for himself.

And in time the director of the prison learned to depend on Joseph. He trusted him so much that he put him in charge of the prison. The Lord was with Joseph and blessed everything he did.

Two prisoners especially interested him. One had been the cupbearer to the king. The other had been the chief baker for the palace.

One morning Joseph noticed that they appeared troubled. "What's the matter?" he asked. "You look upset."

"Both of us have had dreams," they answered. "We're sure they mean something, but there's no one here to tell us what."

"Only God can do that," Joseph replied. "But what did you dream?"

"Well," the cupbearer began, "in my dream I saw a grapevine with three branches. And even as I watched, the branch budded and blossomed, and the grapes ripened!" His eyes grew big with wonder as he remembered what he had seen. No one had ever seen nature move so quickly before.

"I was holding the king's cup," he continued, "and I picked the grapes and squeezed them into the cup and gave it to him." He stopped and looked at his fellow prisoner, a question in his eyes.

In a flash God revealed to Joseph what the dream meant. Without hesitating he said to the cupbearer, "In three days the king will take you out of prison and give you back your office. You will serve the king just as you did before."

Joseph paused, then asked softly, "And when you have your position back, would you please remember me and say a word to help me get out of prison?"

The cupbearer beamed and nodded. "Oh, yes! Yes, of course. I'll remember you, Joseph."

Now the baker tugged at Joseph's arm.

"What about my dream? I dreamed that I was carrying three baskets on my head. The top basket overflowed with all kinds of pastries, and the birds flew to the basket and ate their fill."

A shadow flickered across Joseph's face, and he looked soberly into the baker's eyes. "Your dream will also be fulfilled in three days. At that time the king will release you— and have your head cut off! Then he will hang your body on a pole and the birds will eat your flesh."

The baker stared at Joseph with horror-filled eyes before turning and disappearing into a gloomy corner.

A day went by. Another day passed. On the third day prison guards threw open the gate and called the names of prisoners who would be released in honor of the pharaoh's birthday.

"The king's cupbearer!" the guard called, and the cupbearer, smiling broadly, left the prison without so much as a backward glance at Joseph.

"The king's chief baker!" the guard called. As the baker stumbled from the prison, he turned to stare at Joseph with fear-glazed eyes.

Soon word drifted back to the remaining prisoners. The cupbearer had been reinstated, but the baker had been beheaded and hung in the public square. Birds flocked to his lifeless body to feast upon his flesh.

And Joseph was still a prisoner, far from home. The cup-bearer had forgotten all about him. But God had not.

✕ ✕ ✕

"Oh, no," the children chorused. "What happened next? We have to know."

Professor Appleby laughed as he hurriedly reached for the next tape. "I figured this story would get your hearts racing. Don't worry. I have the second installment right here."

Soon the children could hear splashing sounds again as Maggie B cleared her throat on the sailboat on the Nile and continued her story.

✕ ✕ ✕

The "wise men" and magicians of Egypt stood shaking and perplexed before the throne of the mighty pharaoh. "What do you get paid for if you cannot tell me the meaning of my dreams?" the ruler of Egypt thundered.

"Perhaps if your majesty would be so kind as to tell us the dream once more?" one magician stammered.

Pahraoh glanced at him, his heavy black brows almost touching in an angry scowl. "All right! Once more, and listen carefully," he began again. "I dreamed I was standing by the river, the mighty Nile, giver of life. Seven fat cows, cooling themselves in the water, suddenly waded to the shore and began to feed on the reeds. Then seven skinny cows, their ribs showing and hipbones sticking out like sails on a ship, followed the fat cows and ate them. But they stayed as thin as before.

"Then I had another dream. I saw seven heads of grain, green and ripe, growing on a stalk. Seven other heads of grain, drooping under the blast of the hot desert wind, swallowed up the ripe and healthy grain.

"Now who can tell me what these things mean?"

The magicians and wise men opened their mouths, but no words came out. Baffled, they could only stare at their ruler.

Just then pharaoh's cupbearer, the same one who had promised two years before to speak a good word for Joseph, stepped forward.

"Your Majesty," he quavered, "I must confess this day the wrong I have done to someone who can interpret dreams!" Quickly he told the king about Joseph.

"Send for him!" the king commanded.

At that moment Joseph knelt in prayer in a private corner of the prison. "How much longer, God?" he prayed. He had tried to keep cheerful from day to day, but a lonely, deserted feeling stayed with him, and he longed for home, and his father, and—freedom!

Suddenly the sound of footsteps interrupted his prayer. Looking up, he saw the guard striding toward him.

"Get up!" the guard snapped even before he had reached Joseph. "The king demands your presence. Immediately! Here's a change of clothes for you. When you've finished dressing, someone will shave you." The guard stared in disgust at Joseph's beard, grown long in prison. In Egypt only ignorant foreigners wore beards.

Within minutes Joseph found himself in the palace of Pharaoh. After the gloom of prison, the gleam of gold almost hurt his eyes. He stared in wonder at the costly tapestries and bright murals on the walls and a lavishly painted ceiling portraying Pharaoh's mighty deeds. Everything declared that he was in the throne room of the most powerful king in the world.

And high upon the throne sat the pharaoh, his eyes mere slits as they bored suspiciously into the prisoner.

Joseph bowed before the king, but hardly had time to stand up straight before Pharaoh shot a question at him.

"I understand you can interpret dreams."

"No, I cannot," Joseph answered quickly. "But the God I serve will give the interpretation."

For just an instant the king wondered, *Why should I trust this Hebrew slave who serves a God unknown to Egypt?* But in

Joseph's honest face the king saw something he trusted.

"This is what I dreamed . . ." he began, and told Joseph all about the cows and the grain.

Joseph's eyes never left Pharaoh's, but his mind was on God, and God helped him to understand the strange dream. "You have not had two dreams, but one," Joseph replied promptly, "for they mean the same thing. The next seven years will be good ones for Egypt. Crops will grow and produce a bountiful harvest, but then famine will come. For another seven years the Nile will barely flood the land and water it, so the soil will dry up. Grain will wither and die. People will be hungry, not only in Egypt, but in distant places.

"To prepare for that time, Your Majesty should choose a wise person and put him in charge of the country. Let officials help that person store one fifth of the harvest during the good years. Then when the famine starts, Egypt, and only Egypt, will have a reserve supply of food. If this is not done, people will starve. Death will walk the land."

The king listened, wide-eyed, struck with the wisdom of Joseph's words. After a hurried conference with his advisors, he turned back to the Hebrew slave.

"You, Joseph, will be that man in charge of the country, for in you dwells the spirit of a God. I name you vizier, prime minister of Egypt, second only to me in rank and power. And no one in all the land of Egypt will raise a hand or foot without your permission!"

Soon all Egypt buzzed with the amazing news—a slave had been made vizier, given the king's ring and a gold chain, and dressed in fine linen. A slave, fresh from prison, now rode through their narrow streets in the second royal chariot while, at the king's command, all Egypt bowed low. The pharaoh gave Joseph a new Egyptian name and a wife, Asenath, the daughter of Potiphera, priest of On.

Now 30 years old, Joseph traveled all over the land of Egypt, building storehouses for grain and organizing laborers to harvest the crops for the government. He kept careful records, but after seven years of unequaled harvest, he finally stopped weighing all the grain, for, the Bible says, it was like the sand of the sea.

Then the drought began. In Canaan the land dried up and turned to dust. The skies, usually full of rain in the winter months, shed hardly a drop. Jacob, his beard and hair now white with age, gathered his sons together.

"I have heard," he said, "that there is grain in Egypt. Why don't you go there and bring us back some before we all starve to death?"

The brothers left for Egypt—except for one. Their father kept Benjamin, Rachel's younger son, at home with him. This son reminded him of the wife he had loved best.

As Joseph looked over the list of those who would appear before him to ask for grain that day, his heart suddenly pounded and his hands shook. He recognized the names of his brothers!

Ignoring his scribes, he began to pace back and forth. *Can I possibly forgive them for what they did to me?* he wondered. *What are they like after all these years? I must find out what kind of men they are now!*

One of his servants ushered the 10 brothers from Canaan into the palace, where the vizier sat upon a golden throne on a raised platform. Bowing deeply, they touched their noses to the floor. Watching them, Joseph suddenly remembered his youthful dreams of bowing grain and bending stars.

Desperately he struggled to keep his face from showing his feelings. In a harsh voice he asked in the Egyptian language, "Where are you from?" An interpreter repeated the question.

The brothers looked at the prime minister's stern face and Egyptian clothing and did not recognize Joseph. "We have come from Canaan to buy food," they answered.

Their brother frowned at them. "I believe you are spies!"

Judah's face went white. The penalty for spying was

slavery or death. "No! We are not spies, but honest men!"

Joseph leaned forward, eager to learn more, but fearful of what he might discover. "You are spies," he repeated, "come to plan an invasion of Egypt."

"Not so, sir," the brothers protested. "We were 12 brothers in all, sons of a good man, but one brother is dead and the youngest is in Canaan with our father."

Suddenly Joseph caught his breath. His father was still alive! But he repeated, "You are spies. Only by bringing your youngest brother here can you prove that you are telling the truth."

He motioned toward the palace guards. "Put these men in prison."

After three days the brothers found themselves released from prison and standing once more before the dreaded prime minister.

"Because I am a God-fearing man I will spare your lives on this condition," Joseph stated. "One of you must stay here as a hostage while the rest of you return to your home. When you bring back your youngest brother, I will then know that you are telling the truth."

They talked hurriedly among themselves, not realizing that the prime minister could understand every word they said.

"We'll have to do as he says."

"Our treatment of Joseph has caught up with us," one of them said, remembering events of long ago. "We turned deaf ears to his cries, and that is why we're in trouble now!"

The guilt the brothers had suffered all through the years at last revealed itself.

"I told you not to harm the boy," Reuben protested, "and now we will pay for his death."

Joseph rushed from the room before his brothers could see the grief he could no longer hide.

When he returned, he pointed at Simeon. "Put this one in prison," he commanded. "Sell the others grain and let them go."

Jacob's sons spoke little as they traveled back toward Canaan. When night fell, they made camp. One of the brothers, preparing to feed his donkey, opened his grain sack.

Suddenly he turned a white, shocked face toward the others. "The silver I paid for the grain is in the top of my sack," he gasped. "How did it get there?"

With a feeling of approaching doom the rest opened their sacks. In the top of each sack rested the silver bars they had paid for the grain. Bewildered and frightened, the brothers never imagined that the prime minister had himself returned their money.

At last they reached Canaan and related the whole frightening experience to their old father. Jacob stared at his sons. "You have returned without Simeon, and now you want me to let Benjamin go, too? This strange ruler . . . who knows what he will do next? I will not let Benjamin go!"

"Father, if I don't bring Benjamin back to you, you can kill my two sons!" Reuben replied.

But nothing could convince Jacob to let Rachel's younger son, grown dearer since he lost Joseph, go to Egypt where a monstrous prime minister waited to play cruel games with the lives of his sons.

"Never!" Jacob repeated. "If I lost Benjamin, it would kill me."

4

Joseph's Revenge

As the story ended, the children groaned. "More, more," they called out. "Don't leave us like this!"

Professor Appleby smiled broadly. "I once heard a little girl say that the Bible was boring, not interesting or fun." He glanced at Stacey as he reached for another cassette. "What do you think? Is the Bible boring?"

The girl blushed. "Not when Maggie B tells stories from it," she said softly.

"Oh? And what makes her so interesting?"

Jason lifted his hand. "I know. It's because she really likes 'em too. I can tell."

The old man glanced at his watch, then slipped another tape into the machine. "I think we still have enough time to get back to Joseph and Jacob and the rest of the clan. OK?"

"OK!" three voices chorused excitedly.

In moments Maggie B transported her listeners back to a time when famine gripped a distant land, and a group of men were about to face the greatest challenge of their lives.

✕ ✕ ✕

Levi shook the grain sack, over and over, then stared in dismay at the few kernels that fell to the bottom of the basket.

Benjamin, his eyes round with worry, stepped up behind Levi and gazed first at the nearly empty basket, then at the few remaining sacks of grain.

"How much longer can you put off going to Egypt for more?" Benjamin asked. "We've cut back the animals' feed and our own food as much as we can. Soon we'll be starving."

"I know," Levi answered, eyeing Benjamin's gaunt face.

"That vizier in Egypt insisted that you come with us next time and—"

"No!" The word sounded like the crack of a whip, cutting off Levi's words in midsentence. Jacob stood before them, his bent form straighter than usual, his white hair and beard shining in the sunlight. "I have lost Joseph. Now Simeon lies in prison in a foreign land. You will not take Benjamin from me!"

That evening Jacob and his large family gathered around a small fire.

"Father, listen to us, please," Judah pleaded. One by one the brothers described their starving animals, their hungry children, the dwindling supplies of grain.

"Yes, yes, I know we need more grain, and you must go back to Egypt, but Benjamin stays with me!" Jacob's dark eyes blazed as he looked at his sons.

"But Father!" they exploded, "we won't even get near the vizier unless we take Benjamin with us, and no Egyptian servant would dare to give us grain against his wishes!"

Jacob looked at Benjamin, his hollow cheeks showing how badly he needed food. The old man bowed his head to hide his tears, for he knew he must give in.

"Father," Judah spoke kindly, "I know how much Benjamin means to you, but we must take him with us. I will guard him with my own life. If I don't bring him safely back to you, you can blame me for as long as I live."

"All right!" Jacob's words trembled. "Go to Egypt so that we may have bread." His voice broke, and he just managed to whisper the words, "And take Benjamin. If I must bear the anguish of my children's deaths, so be it."

The brothers loaded their donkeys with a few meager presents of honey, pistachio nuts, and almonds.

"Remember to give them to the vizier," Jacob worried. "And take enough silver to pay back what you found in your sacks after the last journey, plus enough to pay for more grain. Now take your brother and come back as soon as you can with both Benjamin and Simeon. May God bless you and impress the vizier to treat you with kindness!" Jacob turned to his tent.

Joseph, standing on the flat roof of his house, suddenly spotted a dusty little caravan. As the donkeys and men came closer, he recognized his brothers. Hastily, he counted. One, two, three . . . 10 in all. That meant Benjamin had come with them. At least his brothers had not killed him!

"Asenath! Asenath!" he shouted, hurrying down the stairs to the courtyard where his wife sat at the edge of the reflecting pool, sipping a drink and swinging her bare feet in the water.

She looked up, startled. "What is it?"

"Asenath, my brothers have returned, and this time they've brought my own mother's son, my brother

Benjamin!" Excitement filled his wide, dark eyes.

Gradually he calmed down and began to talk, more to himself than to his wife. "I have to know how they treat Benjamin. Are they bullying him the way they did me? If my father favors him as he did me—and he probably does—do they resent it and mistreat him?"

Abruptly he stopped talking and strode to the door. "Sep!" he called, and a servant came running. "This is what I want you to do . . ."

Several hours later Jacob's sons fearfully approached an Egyptian servant, wondering if they would be seized as slaves.

"We were here before," they quickly explained as they extended shaky hands filled with silver, "and we paid for grain we received, but when we opened our sacks we found our money in them! We don't know how it happened, but we have brought back every piece."

"Don't worry," the servant shrugged, "it must have been a miracle because I remember taking your money myself. Now, if you will come with me, the prime minister has invited you to eat in his house. Your brother Simeon will join you."

The brothers stared at each other in bewilderment. Then clutching their gifts, they almost tiptoed behind the servant as he led them through a garden with date palms and fig trees, past a little pond with flocks of birds, and into Joseph's own beautiful home. As they sat down in their dusty robes on cushioned chairs, the servant brought water and washed their feet. No one said anything as they stared at each other, wondering what would happen next.

Before long another servant ushered them into a large banqueting room with tables and stools, but the brothers noticed only one thing—the powerful prime minister!

Bowing before Joseph like sheaves of grain in the wind, the brothers again did not recognize this stately "Egyptian" vizier.

"Arise," Joseph commanded, careful not to look at

Benjamin. "How is your health?" he asked.

Nervously the brothers answered that they were well.

"And how is your father, of whom you spoke?" Joseph continued, trying hard to keep the eagerness from his voice.

"Our father is in good health," the brothers answered cautiously.

Joseph could no longer keep his eyes off Benjamin—his own younger brother standing before him after all these years. He noted the thin cheeks, a sure sign of the widespread famine. As he gazed into the dark eyes, so like his own and his mother's, Joseph suddenly ran from the room.

At last Joseph returned and, with a wave of his hand, directed the servants to serve the meal.

The brothers found themselves seated around a large table. Palm fronds, to brush the flies away, lay within easy reach.

Puzzled looks crossed their faces as they suddenly realized that Reuben, the oldest, sat at the head of the table. Next to him came Simeon, then Levi, then all the other brothers in order of their ages. Last was Benjamin, the youngest. *How does he know our ages?* the brothers asked themselves as they stared fearfully at their host.

But they had little time to wonder, for the servants began bringing the meal. The brothers stared as mounds of meat, heaps of vegetables, stacks of melon, baskets of bread, piles of pastries, and jugs of wine appeared. But for every piece of food the servants gave the brothers, they brought Benjamin five.

Seated at his separate table, Joseph studied his brothers carefully. How would they react as they saw Benjamin favored? Would the old jealousy spring up? Would they mutter under their breaths and complain that Benjamin had five times as much food as they did?

But Reuben and Issachar and Gad and even Simeon smiled as they watched Benjamin enjoying the feast. At the end of the meal the brothers felt relaxed—and full! They still did not understand this strange Egyptian, but he had treated them like guests. They decided that God had answered Jacob's prayers.

And Joseph, almost believing that his cruel brothers had changed, decided to test them just once more. Calling his servants, he instructed them, "Fill the men's sacks with as much food as they can carry, and put each man's money in the top of his sack. Then put my own silver cup in the sack of the youngest brother."

The next morning the brothers arose with the sun, and humming happily, loaded their donkeys with bulging sacks of grain. They thought of how pleased Jacob would be to see them return, loaded with food, and with Benjamin well and unhurt.

When they reached the edge of the city, the brothers looked back in surprise as they heard the sound of hoofbeats. Servants of the prime minister surrounded them with their chariots. Jumping to the ground, they shouted, "Why have you stolen our master's silver cup?"

"St—stolen a silver cup?" the Hebrews stammered, too surprised even to think clearly.

"Yes," a servant answered, "the one he drinks from! Why have you acted so shamefully when he treated you so well?"

Now the brothers found their tongues. "We swear that we have stolen nothing. How could you even think such a thing? You know that we brought back money to you from Canaan that had been returned to us. This whole idea is ridiculous. Search us. If you find this silver cup, we'll all be your slaves!"

"We'll search, all right," the servant answered coldly, "but only the man who has the cup will return as a slave."

Then the Egyptians pulled the grain sacks off the backs of the donkeys. The Hebrews' faces turned white as once again they spotted the silver they had paid for their grain winking up at them from their own sacks.

But when the servants opened Benjamin's sack the

brothers' hearts nearly stopped, for there, nestled in the grain, rested the vizier's silver goblet. Feeling as if they moved in a nightmare, Joseph's brothers reloaded their donkeys and headed once more toward the palace and the wrath of the Egyptian prime minister.

✕ ✕ ✕

"One more, one more," the three children pleaded when the third tape ended. "We can stay for a few more minutes—honest."

Professor Appleby glanced out the window and studied the sunlight slanting through the forest. The rain had ended.

"Your moms will start to get worried soon," he said.

"But we can run all the way home," Jason protested. "We'll get back in time for supper. Really. Just play us the last tape. Please?"

The old man nodded. "OK. But this is the last one for today. Then you have to run along. I don't want your parents getting upset with me. Then they might not let you stop by anymore."

With a smile he fitted the fourth and last tape into his machine as the children settled back into their chairs to listen.

✕ ✕ ✕

Once again the 11 sons of Jacob bowed themselves to the floor before the prime minister of Egypt. Their hearts hammered in their chests, and they trembled with fear.

Joseph, his lips pressed together in a thin, angry line, fixed them with a cold stare.

"What have you done?" he snapped. "Stealing my own cup! Don't you know better than to try to deceive me?"

Judah struggled to his feet.

"My lord," he pleaded, bowing once more. "We don't know what to say or how to clear ourselves. Surely our God must be punishing us for past sins." At those words all the brothers remembered the cruel, unspeakable crime they had committed against Joseph. But they had no idea that he was standing right before them.

"We will all be your slaves, not just he with whom the cup was found," Judah continued.

Smoothly Joseph replied, "Oh, no. The rest of you can go free. Only the thief will be my slave." *And will they?* Joseph wondered. *Will they choose to leave Benjamin here as a slave, not caring what happens to him or that my father will grieve?*

"Oh, my lord," Judah implored, edging closer to Joseph, "I beg of you to listen to me and not be angry, for your power is equal to Pharaoh's." Once more he bowed deeply before Joseph.

"You asked us about our family, and we told you of our father and the child of his old age. That boy, our brother Benjamin, is the only living child of his mother. Our father loves him like his own soul.

"You asked us to bring Benjamin here to Egypt, and we did. But our father grieved at the thought of his coming and said, 'You know that my wife, Rachel, gave birth to two sons. One has been torn to pieces by a wild animal, and now, if you take Benjamin from me, and harm comes to him, I will go with sorrow to the grave.'

"Now you ask us to return to our father without him. How can we face our father without Benjamin and watch him die from grief? I swore that I would protect Benjamin with my life, so I beg you, let me take his place as a slave and let Benjamin go home with his brothers."

Joseph stood motionless during Judah's plea. Only a tiny muscle twitched in his smooth face, but he felt his heart would burst. He had his answer! Judah's words, the silent plea in the eyes of his other brothers, proved to Joseph that the evil men who had plotted murder and sold their own brother as a slave had changed.

With a sudden cry Joseph commanded his servants and the interpreter to leave the room.

Then, facing his brothers, with tears running down his cheeks, he proclaimed in their own language, "I am Joseph! Oh, tell me everything about my father!"

But the brothers heard only "I am Joseph!" The words roared in their ears. How could this vizier of the most powerful land on earth be their brother, Joseph? And if he were, what dreadful thing would he do to them to get even for their terrible deed?

But Joseph stood with his arms outstretched. "Come close, I beg you. I *am* Joseph, whom you sold into Egypt. Don't be hard on yourselves for what you did, for God prepared the way before me.

"For two years famine has swept the land and for five more years the plows will roll up dust, and the few withered stalks that grow will produce no grain. For this reason God sent me to Egypt—that you and your children might live."

Slowly Joseph's brothers remembered the dreams of a young boy, dreams they had determined would never come true. Yet here they were, bowing before him, depending on him for their very lives.

"God has made me the advisor to Pharaoh himself, and a ruler throughout all of Egypt," their brother continued. "Now hurry, go to my father and tell him I am alive and ruler of Egypt. Tell him to come to me, quickly, and live near me. You shall have the land of Goshen, an area of rich soil.

"Bring your wives and children, and their children, and your flocks and herds, and everything you own. Come back quickly so that you will not suffer more from the famine. Tell my father that I will provide him with all good things in life and care for him."

Then he flung his arms around Benjamin, and the two brothers who had not seen each other for more than 20 years clung to each other. Afterward, one by one, Joseph hugged all his brothers.

Far into the night the 12 sons of Jacob talked, trying to

catch up on all that had happened since they had last seen each other.

Soon word reached Pharaoh that Joseph's brothers had returned to Egypt. The whole palace buzzed with the news. Everyone knew that Joseph had been a slave, but until now no one had known that he was the son of a respected nomad in the land of Canaan. Pharaoh was delighted to learn of Joseph's good fortune.

Words tumbled from the king's lips as he burst into Joseph's presence, "Tell your brothers to load up their donkeys, go to Canaan, and bring your father down here to Egypt, and we'll give them some of our best land. We'll send wagons to help move their goods, but tell them not to bother bringing everything. That would only slow them down, and they can get more here."

Joseph smiled, glad that the king agreed with his own plan.

As the brothers prepared to return to Canaan, Joseph handed each of them a beautiful, brand new robe. But to Benjamin he gave five new robes as well as 300 shekels of silver. And all the brothers smiled happily at Benjamin without a trace of jealousy.

But Joseph had not forgotten his father. To Jacob he sent 10 donkeys loaded down with all kinds of good things from Egypt, and then 10 more donkeys bearing food—grain and bread and other things to keep them from being hungry on their trip back to Egypt.

At home in Canaan Jacob sat dozing in the sun, dreaming of happier days when little Joseph tagged barefoot at his heels while Rachel smiled from a tent opening. Suddenly he heard donkeys braying, hoofbeats, and loud, excited voices.

The patriarch sprang to his feet as fast as his old bones and lame hip would let him. His sons, mounted on donkeys, reined up before him. Other donkeys followed, laden with bulging sacks. Splendid wagons pulled by oxen trailed along behind them.

Jacob's daughters-in-law, grandchildren, and servants came running from all directions. Food from Egypt was their only thought, but Jacob's sons had a surprise for them far better than food.

"Father," they spoke gently, when the excitement had died down a bit, "we have some news for you, and we think you'd better sit down."

"What is it?" Jacob asked, startled. His first thought upon his sons' arrival had been to look for Benjamin. The son now stood before him, well and happy. And Simeon had returned. Food—more food than he had imagined his sons might bring—overflowed the donkeys' backs. What news could there be?

Carefully, slowly, Judah said, "Father, Joseph is alive, and he is the prime minister of Egypt!"

The old man's heart went numb. What cruel joke were his sons playing on him? *Joseph, oh, Joseph!* he thought. *If only it were true!*

Haltingly the sons of Israel explained all that had happened. They told the story of their evil deed, of the Ishmaelite slave traders, of Joseph's imprisonment, and finally, their reunion with their brother. "Look at the wagons, Father. Joseph gave them to us. Look at the clothes, at Benjamin's silver. Look at all the extra food and animals. Our brother Joseph sent them to you because he wants us to move to Egypt and live near him. He especially wants to see you, Father."

Nearly speechless with joy and amazement, Jacob listened, his faded eyes never leaving their faces. "I *will* go to Egypt!" he said finally. "My son Joseph, my dear son Joseph yet lives, and I will see him before I die!"

✕ ✕ ✕

The voice on the tape recorder faded away.

Stacey, Maria, and Jason rose slowly to their feet, broad

smiles creasing their young faces.

"Thank you, Professor Appleby," Jason sighed. "I could listen to Maggie B all day long."

"Well, you almost did," the professor chuckled as he walked with them out onto the front porch. "Now you must hurry home to your parents. It's suppertime. Don't want them to worry."

With a wave the children turned to leave. "See ya tomorrow. You've got more tapes, haven't you?"

"Lots of 'em," the old man called after them. "Tomorrow we'll meet some spies."

The trio of children disappeared into the forest as the old man turned and made his way back into the mansion resting by the little clearing. The early-afternoon rain had stopped long ago, leaving the colorful autumn foliage fresh and clean.

HIDDEN MEANINGS

Hiding in the six blocks of letters are some things that really made a difference in Joseph's life. Choose one letter from each block of letters to spell out the word that identifies them. Can you find the hidden word?

V W P	I O L	S R A	I K N	A I N	N N I
G P P	R R H	A A A	I Y R	N I O	L N H
J D P	A R O	C E T	O A I	B M P	R S H

Answer: ____ ____ ____ ____ ____ ____

⑤
Spies and Falling Walls

Jason studied the statue thoughtfully, his chin resting on the tabletop. Before him stood a stone man, perhaps six inches tall, sporting a pointed hat and what looked like a cloth skirt.

In one hand the little man gripped a long spear. The other held an oblong shield. A broad knife hung from his belt, and on his feet he wore thick leather sandals.

"Is he very, very old?" the boy questioned, his eyes not leaving the statue.

"Not really," Professor Appleby shook his head. "When an archaeologist discovers statues like that, they usually end up in a museum or safely tucked away in some university. That's a copy of an ancient soldier found in the land we call Israel. Maggie B discovered it while digging around the ruins of old Jericho about a year ago. She had an artist in Jerusalem make this little statue so she could show me what she'd found."

"That reminds me," Maria called from across the room where she was admiring a long line of camels carved from olive wood. "Didn't you tell us you had a picture of Maggie B? You forgot to show it to us yesterday. Remember?"

Professor Appleby's eyebrows rose. "Well, I certainly did say that."

"Can we help you look for it?" the children asked.

The old man chuckled. "No telling where that photograph might be. I'd probably misplace you guys if I took you through the house looking for it."

Professor Appleby thought for a moment. "Tell you what. Let me start the next tape, and I'll look while you listen. How's that sound?"

Stacey, Maria, and Jason hurried to their favorite chairs by the fireplace. The warm flames flickered in the deep stone hearth, doing a fine job of chasing the autumn chill from the air.

The old man adjusted the settings on his tape recorder and slipped a cassette into place. "Now, there's something you need to know," he said. "This story begins with the death of one of God's great leaders. The man had led a nation of people across a hot desert and brought them to a wonderful new Promised Land. But something happened, and a new leader had to take his place. Understand?"

"We understand," came the quick reply.

With a smile Professor Appleby pressed the play button and waited. When he heard noises rattling from the tiny speaker, he nodded and left the room to search for his family photo album.

The listeners heard the whistling of the wind as the tiny tape slid past the machine's playback head. Then they heard Maggie B clear her throat and begin.

✗ ✗ ✗

Night fell on the uneasy camp of the Israelites. Before hundreds of flickering campfires families gathered and talked in hushed and wondering tones. Where had Moses gone? Why hadn't he come back to camp?

All the Israelites had their own story to tell of how they had last seen him. "He had his rod with him, and he walked across the plain toward Mount Nebo."

"I saw him going up the mountain. He climbed fast, looking up the whole time."

Joshua said nothing, but he remembered watching Moses gradually fading into the distance until he could see him no more.

Long after others slept, Joshua stared into his campfire. The flickering flames died slowly, leaving here and there a faintly glowing ember. Still he squatted by the smoldering ashes, remembering his good friend and thinking about his new responsibilities.

Then in the stillness of the night God spoke to him. "Moses is dead, and you are the new leader, the one who will guide My people into the Promised Land. Be strong and brave. Remind the people to obey My every law.

"If you will do these things, you will conquer all the land I promised to your ancestors. Remember—I am with you wherever you go."

In the morning Joshua called the people together. Whispering among themselves, anxious to hear his words, they hurried to an open place in front of the tabernacle courtyard. There stood Joshua. The sun beat down on his curly black hair and beard, and a gentle breeze rippled the robe covering his square-built, muscular body.

He waited, stiff and straight, every inch a soldier. Only his eyes moved as they swept the congregation with a sorrowful gaze. Then he spoke, softly but clearly. "Moses is dead."

A gasp, a cry, a long, low moan escaped the crowd. Many tore their clothes in anguish.

"Please," Joshua at last spoke over the commotion, "listen to my words. We will mourn the death of Moses, but the Lord is still with us. In just a little while we will enter the Promised Land!"

For 30 days the people mourned for Moses, realizing at last how much they had actually loved the man of God. Word spread throughout the camp, "There has never been another prophet like Moses, for the Lord talked to him face-to-face."

On a cool, dark morning before the sun had risen, two men quietly made their way to Joshua's tent. "Come in quickly," Joshua whispered as they approached. "I don't want any curious eyes or ears to witness our conversation."

Wonderingly the men stared at their new leader. Why had he summoned them?

"I want you two men to cross the Jordan while it is still

dark," he said as if reading their minds. "Enter the city of Jericho and find out all about it. How many people live there? Are they prepared for an attack?

"Examine the city walls. Are they in good repair? Where might there be a weakness? Come back when you have found out everything possible. And remember, report only to me. Don't talk to the people, not even your own wives, about this. Now go with God's blessing!"

Joshua watched the men silently slip away into the night. He remembered all too well the spy mission he had been a part of 40 years before. He would take no chances on a bad report causing another uprising among the people.

Silently, stealthily, just as Joshua had instructed, the spies made their way to the Jordan. Feeling their way along its stony bank, they waded deep into the current. Venus, a pale light in the brightening sky, gazed down at them as they felt the black water rise to their armpits. Struggling to keep their feet under them, they at last climbed out on the opposite bank and waited for the first gray streaks of dawn.

Reaching the walled city of Jericho, they mingled with a crowd approaching the now open city gate. Ducking their heads and pulling their headcloths low over their faces, they slipped in amid the noise and bustle.

Once inside, they cautiously separated themselves from the group and darted down a dim, narrow street. All through the day they listened and observed, pretending to browse in the market, occasionally buying a few things.

As night fell, they felt suspicious eyes upon them and realized that they must find shelter—fast. But where?

Then they remembered one house where they had seen men of every description coming and going all day, and even more since night had fallen. Built high on the thick city wall, it commanded a view in every direction.

"Let's go there!" one whispered to the other, and staying close to the wall, they hurried toward the house. Almost feverishly they climbed the steps and banged on the door.

The door swung open, and a pretty woman with sad eyes and a painted smile stood before them. She did not seem surprised to see them. "Come in," she murmured in a husky voice.

The two Israelites stared at the woman who entertained men for pay. Before they could say a word, she said, "My name is Rahab. Let me bring you a drink, and then we can talk."

"Wait!" one of the spies said. "We want nothing from you except a place to stay for the night."

Rahab looked at them sharply, then her features relaxed. "I know who you are!" she suddenly exclaimed. "You're Israelites, aren't you? Everyone here has heard of the Israelites and of their God who dries up seas and crushes armies." She was about to say more when loud voices and a pounding on the door interrupted her.

"Let us in, by order of the king!" someone shouted.

Without a word she pointed to a staircase leading to the roof of her house. The spies quickly understood and scrambled up the stone steps.

Then Rahab leaned against her door and sweetly drawled, "You'll have to wait just a moment. You've caught me at a bad time." She laughed softly for the soldiers' benefit, then wheeled and raced up the stairs to the roof where the two strangers stood in the starlight.

"Quick!" she hissed. "Get down! But don't stay close together. If they discover one of you, they might not find the other." Silently she grabbed armloads of flax spread out to dry, and piled it first over one spy, then the other. Then, kicking the spread-out flax with her feet so that the other bunches looked no different from the piles hiding the two men, she gave a quick backward glance and hurried down the stairs.

Unbolting the door, she opened it wide and smiled at the glaring officers. "Won't you come in, gentlemen?" she purred. "Whatever brings so many of you in such a hurry?"

"Where are they?" the head officer shouted. "The spies! We've had word that two Israelites, sent here to find out how best to attack Jericho, were seen coming into your house."

Rahab hesitated for only a split second. What, after all, were these strangers to her? Why should she risk her life for them? But in their honest faces she had seen something she wanted—a chance for a better life.

"They were here earlier," she answered smoothly, "but they left. Search the house if you wish," she invited with a charming smile.

The officers looked at her, scowled, grumbled, then turned and stomped away.

Rahab waited until she was sure they would not return, then rushed back up the stairs to the roof. "You can come out now," she announced in a loud whisper.

The men squirmed out of the flax, pieces of it sticking out

of their hair and ears and clothes. Rahab put her hand over her mouth to hold back a chuckle. They did look funny!

But she soon grew serious as the two Israelites thanked her again and again for hiding them. "I protected you because of your God," she told them. "Everyone knows that Israel is going to attack Jericho, and everyone is afraid of your people."

The men smiled a little at the idea—Israel with its few weapons and without even a trained army. But they did have God, the best weapon of all.

Rahab was looking at them with a new light in her eyes. "I believe," she said seriously, "that your God is the supreme God of heaven, unlike the gods of any other nation. Now I ask you this one thing. Swear to me by the sacred name of your God that when Jericho is conquered, you will let me live, along with my family. In this way you can repay me for helping you."

"We promise to do as you have asked, if you will not betray us. Your lives for ours!" the spies assured her.

She smiled briefly, then reached for a long red rope. "I will let you down over the wall with this," she explained while quickly tying the rope around a small wooden beam projecting from the mud-brick wall.

"When you reach the ground, run and hide yourselves in the mountains. Hide there for three days, because the soldiers will be looking for you in the city. Then go on your way."

The first man grasped the rope, mouthed a quick "thank you!" and disappeared over the ledge. As the second spy grabbed the rope, one leg on the window ledge, he turned to Rahab. "The only way we can protect you is if all the Israelite soldiers recognize your house. So that they will know which one is yours, lower this same scarlet cord from the window. When we see it, we will not harm anyone in this house."

Then grasping the rope in both hands, he swung out over the ledge and vanished from view.

Rahab slowly pulled the rope back inside her window. But she didn't untie it. *I'll lower it again when the time comes!* she told herself. *I believe that the God of the Israelites is the supreme God. He will save me and my family!* And He did.

In years to come all Israel would remember the kindness and bravery of Rahab. And her life would never again be the same. She would learn to love God more and more, and eventually marry an Israelite man.

And through Rahab's descendants would be born the Promised One, the One God had promised to Adam and Eve so long ago.

✗ ✗ ✗

"Professor!" Jason called out. "Hey Professor Appleby. The story ended. We need the next tape."

No answer.

Maria scratched her head. "You think he's lost?"

"In his own house?" Jason asked, a knowing grin bending the corners of his mouth. "I guess that's possible with our new friend. Maybe we'd better start the next tape without him. He could be gone all afternoon."

Stacey nodded and dug through the small pile of cassettes the professor had left on the table by the door. "Here it is. *The Capture of Jericho.* I think this one's next."

Jason pushed the tape into the machine. The unseen Maggie B adjusted some papers.

✗ ✗ ✗

Tramp—tramp—tramp.

The Israelites marched around the city of Jericho while seven priests blew harsh, earsplitting blasts on trumpets made of rams' horns.

Inside the immense walls people nervously asked each other, "What are they doing? Our army is prepared for an attack—so why don't the Israelites attack?"

The soldiers of Jericho stood on the walls, armed with

bows and arrows, slings, spears, and swords. Others, dressed in full armor, held the reins of restless horses already harnessed to war chariots. The huge city gate stood shut, bolted, and guarded. Jericho was prepared for war, but how could it fight against an army that only marched around their city, never coming quite close enough to reach with their sling stones and arrows?

The king of Jericho, a squat man with wild white hair and pale eyes, held his hands over his ears and moaned. He felt a terrible sense of doom. "Rebah!" he called, and his wife stepped through the doorway, regarding him with cool, gray eyes.

"Yes?" she asked, noting with disgust his cowardly posture.

"Rebah, I feel sure we are going to die at the hands of these Israelites. They worship a god more powerful than—" He stopped, not quite daring to speak ill of the Canaanite gods, Baal and Asherah.

"Why don't you say it?" his wife challenged. "They worship a god more powerful than ours! Have Baal or Asherah ever parted a sea, or sent food from the sky, or made water pour from a rock as we've heard the Israelite God has done? Have they ever given us victory over armies better trained and armed than our own?

"You've had weeks, even months, to throw yourself on the mercy of the Israelites and accept their God. After all, you've seen how powerful their God is, and you've heard how He takes special care of His people. Perhaps it's not too late, even now! Why don't you surrender, and worship the God of Israel?"

But the king only stared at her through fear-glazed eyes, afraid to turn his back on his gods, but terrified of Yahweh, God of the Israelites.

And so he sat, hands over his ears, rocking and moaning. Outside the city the long line of Israelites continued to circle Jericho.

Each morning as dawn streaked the sky, dim, gray forms stepped out of the mist, and the march began. Armed Israelite soldiers led the procession, followed by seven priests blowing rams' horns. Just behind these priests came seven more, carrying a sacred, gleaming object—the ark of the covenant.

Following the instructions Joshua had received from God, the army marched without uttering a word, not even a whisper. Only the tramping of feet and the nervewracking blare of ram's horns disturbed the terrible silence. After they had circled the city once, the Israelites withdrew swiftly, silently, to their own camp.

As they arrived, those who did not take part in the procession swarmed around the soldiers. "Did anything happen?"

"How much longer will you just march around the city?"

"Tell us again what Joshua said!"

And the soldiers repeated the instructions the Commander of the Lord's army had given to Joshua. "We are to march around once every day for six days. On the seventh day we will go around the city seven times. Then the ram's horns will blow one long, loud blast, we will all shout, and the city will be ours!"

"But how? What will happen?"

Softly the soldiers answered, "Joshua said the walls of the city will fall down."

Eyes round with wonder, the people stared first at the soldiers, then at Jericho. How could those massive walls, built many cubits thick of solid brick, just collapse? But God had said they would, and they now trusted Him.

Children ran off to play "Walls of Jericho." Gathering stones, they built a tiny walled city, complete with ramp and lookout towers. Then they gathered bits of palm fronds and sticks, and stuck them on top of the walls for "soldiers."

"Now," cried one youngster, "I'm Joshua. Everybody march around the city!" Quickly they formed a line, the "soldiers" marching five across, just as the real soldiers did.

JERICHO JUMBLE

You're an Israelite soldier, and you've just helped capture Jericho! With four other soldiers you must guide Rahab and her family to safety. Everything's in an uproar, and you've temporarily lost your four friends somewhere inside the fallen walls of the city. Can you get to each of your friends—without retracing your steps or using a street more than once—before getting to Rahab's house?

Little "priests" carried a make-believe ark while others tooted through their cupped hands, imitating the sound of a ram's horn.

"It's the seventh day!" announced the make-believe Joshua, and the "priests" tooted vigorously. Then the children shouted loud enough to scare themselves, and with some well-aimed kicks, the "walls of Jericho" tumbled down.

As the children shrieked with laughter, their mothers and fathers smiled. But just a short distance away the real walls of Jericho stood strong as a mountain, daring anyone to budge them.

Inside those city walls the people grew more nervous, more frustrated. For six days the Israelites had kept up that dreadful marching. Even when they returned to camp, the echoes of their tramping seemed to linger. And the people's ears rang with the sounds of ram's horns.

Perhaps most disturbing of all, however, was the strange boxlike object carried by the priests. Its golden lid gleamed in the sunshine. But a brighter light, the light of God's presence, also seemed to surround it. The people of Jericho feared that light. They had never before seen anything like it.

The seventh morning dawned. Gray figures marched out of the mist and began their fearful tramping. Mournful blasts on the ram's horns alerted the uneasy citizens of Jericho that enemy forces once more surrounded their city.

The soldiers of Jericho steeled themselves for another day of watching the strange, foreboding sight. At last, when the sun had climbed above the eastern mountains, the Israelite soldiers completed their first trip around the city. Nervously Jericho waited for the army to withdraw.

But the soldiers never slowed their pace. They never halted, never turned to this side or that. Instead they just marched. Silently. Wordlessly. The sound of ram's horns scraped the air, and footsteps—thousands of footsteps— echoed across the land. For the second time they tramped around the city.

Now the people of Jericho felt their hearts racing with fear. What did it all mean? "Oh, Baal," some cried, "protect us from the strange soldiers with the strange god." But Baal, of course, had no ears to hear, no mind to think, and no power to do anything. Many clung to their little idols of Asherah, promising all kinds of sacrifices if she would only hear them. But she, like Baal, could neither hear nor help.

A third time the Israelites circled the city. A fourth. The ark shone with a heavenly luster. Now they rounded Jericho for the fifth time. The king paced back and forth on the wall, his lips moving wordlessly, hands to his ears.

The sun hung above the city like a giant eye, then slowly rolled toward the western hills. A sixth time the Israelite army marched, and their own hearts hammered in time with their fearless feet. Soon—*soon* God would reveal His power!

For the seventh time that day the Israelites began their trek around Jericho. The ark glowed, the priests blew, and still they marched. Soldiers atop the walls stared down in a nameless horror, hands slack upon their weapons, sweat bathing their brows.

Tramp, tramp, tramp, tramp. Then a pause. Complete silence.

Suddenly a long, loud blast of ram's horns splinters the air. Joshua cries "Shout!" and the air filled with the thunder of triumphant voices. The huge brown walls of Jericho begin to tremble, crack, crumble. Tons of rock-hard mud groan, heave, and crash to the earth with a mighty roar.

Coughing, choking, the victorious Israelites fight their way through dust and over rubble as they swarm into the city. Frantically they search for one little house, a house with a red cord dangling from a window. At last they find it.

By now flames from hurled torches race along the streets, licking hungrily at anything that will burn. Soldiers bang savagely on the door of the little home. Rahab, pale but composed, flings it open and motions her family to follow the Israelites. "I knew you'd come," she says simply. Quickly the men lead her and her family out of the blazing city to safety.

The spies had kept their promise. And God had kept His, just as He always does.

✕ ✕ ✕

"I found it. I found it!" Professor Appleby burst into the den, hair and arms covered with cobwebs and dust.

Jason removed the tape from the recorder and switched off the machine. "Is there a picture of Maggie B in there?" he asked, eyeing the thick volume the old man was holding.

"You bet there is. Lots of 'em. Gather 'round, and I'll show you."

The children joined the professor at the broad table by the window. They watched as he placed the album gently on the smooth wooden surface and opened it reverently.

Rows of black-and-white and color photos greeted their gaze as the man flipped from one page to another. Finally he paused.

"There she is," he called out. "This was taken about a year ago when she was traveling with a group of Bedouin in Jordan. See the tents? the camels? the goats?"

The children leaned forward and looked into the eyes of a slender, almost frail woman standing before the opening to a large tent. The face was tanned and deeply lined with years. Stray curls of snow-white hair swirled about it like drifts encircling a weather-worn mountain boulder.

But the most eye-catching part of the image was the smile. The three youngsters found themselves smiling back in response to the warm and friendly grin radiating from the dusty page.

"That's her," Professor Appleby said softly. "That's my Maggie B in all her glory."

Maria looked up at the old man, then back at the photo. "She doesn't look like you," the girl said.

"Well, I hope not!" the professor gasped. "She's much better looking than I'll ever be. And can you beat that smile? It's like oil on troubled waters, like a cool breeze in the summer. Everyone who meets her falls in love with her gentle ways." The old man gazed at the picture.

Jason studied the image for a long moment. Then he looked up into Professor Appleby's kind eyes. "You're right, Professor," he said. "She is beautiful."

The old man nodded and sighed. "Don't get to see her much, with her wandering all over the world as she does. But I can listen to the tapes. Her voice assures me that she's well. I'm always glad to hear from her."

"Speaking of tapes," Stacey smiled. "How 'bout tomorrow afternoon? Will you have another one ready for us?"

"You bet," Professor Appleby chuckled. "Maggie B sent a very interesting story about a month ago. It's about Joshua and a bunch of people who tried to trick him—and God. You'll be surprised at what happened."

Chattering with excitement, the children bid farewell, hurried down the stairs, and headed for the forest. The old man watched them go until the leaves hid them from view.

Returning to the den, he paused at the table and gazed down at the smiling face in the picture. "Hey, Maggie B," he said softly. "They like you and your stories."

The old man closed the book and pressed it against his chest. "Your crazy old brother loves you. Don't forget that, ever."

Professor Appleby turned and walked out of the den, leaving the crackling fire to cast its glow on the tapestries and trinkets sent by the smiling woman in the picture.

Jericho

Jericho, whose name may mean "moon," may be one of the oldest inhabited cities in the world. Located five miles north of the Dead Sea and 14 miles from Jerusalem, it is more than 700 feet below sea level. It has a mild, semitropical climate during the winter, but can become extremely hot during the summer. While only about six inches of rain fall on the hot desert plain each year, the oasis' rich soil is watered by the largest spring in Palestine. It flows down the wadi Qelt to the Jordan River six miles away. The Old Testament called it the "city of palms," and even today it still has many palm trees. Jericho has always been a green spot in a blinding white desert landscape.

The city has occupied different sites during the centuries. The ruins of the Old Testament city form a 10-acre mound on the northwest outskirts of the modern city.

Scripture says that Jericho was the first place captured by the Israelites after they crossed the Jordan River. For many years archaeologists thought they had found the ruins of the city Joshua had captured. Then, as they more carefully dated the ruins, they decided that the ruined walls they had uncovered were for the wrong period. Some even argued that there was not even a city of any size there during the time of Joshua—that the Bible writer was making up the story of Joshua's capture of Jericho.

Part of the problem was that archaeologists were looking for the evidence for Joshua's destruction of Jericho during the wrong time period. They had been dating it several centuries after the time the Bible chronology would put it.

About 1410 B.C. the city was unexpectedly destroyed. The upper walls collapsed on the lower ones, making it possible for an invader to enter the city easily. The ruins were full of grain—some of it burned by fires started by the collapsing buildings. The destruction of the city must have happened soon after the spring harvest, the time of the year Joshua marched around the city. None of the grain was taken by invaders. God had told the Israelites to take nothing from the city. Thus the evidence from archaeology matches the biblical story.

6

The Gibeonite Deception

The next day the children arrived at the old mansion soon after school let out. When they knocked at the tall wooden door, there was no answer.

"Strange," Jason said, trying to peek through the dust-coated windows. "I don't think the professor's even home. At least I don't hear him stumbling around inside, and there's no sign of him out here. What's up?"

Something caught Stacey's eye at the far end of the broad porch. "Look," she called out excitedly. "There's the tape recorder and a cassette sitting on the railing."

They hurried in the direction the girl had pointed. Sure enough, the professor's machine and a single cassette rested by a table surrounded by three freshly cleaned and scrubbed metal chairs. A note, held firmly by a stone, waited beside the cassette player.

Quickly Maria picked it up and began to read.

"'Dear Kids: Had to go into town. Expecting a new box tomorrow. Wanted to make sure when it would be delivered.

"'I've left the tape recorder and Maggie B's cassette on the porch. Enjoy the story. Be back soon.

"'Your friend, Professor Appleby.'"

Jason slipped the tape into the machine, and the children settled themselves around the table. As before, wind sounds echoed from the tiny speaker, and then the woman with the pretty smile began her next story.

✕ ✕ ✕

People all over the land of Canaan shivered with fear and shook with anger. Israelites had invaded the land, defeating mighty armies, overthrowing Jericho, and (at last) conquering Ai. And they had gathered on Mount Ebal, declaring the law of their God as the new law of the land in Canaan.

Now the kings from many different little kingdoms in Canaan met together, darting suspicious glances at one another. They remembered all too well the times they had fought each other. Only their fear of the Israelites had brought them together.

A short, grizzled man, king of the Amorites, stood and caught their attention. Everyone listened as he declared, "You all know why we're holding this meeting. The Israelites must be stopped. Our only hope is to defend each other against them."

All the kings agreed, bragging noisily about what they'd do to the Israelite rabble. Finally the Perizzites, the Jebusites, the Amorites, the Hittites, and all the kings from the little kingdoms said farewell and went their separate ways. But the head of one city, small but important as a defender of others around it, had not attended that meeting. The commander of Gibeon decided it would be better to surrender than fight. But what would happen to the Gibeonites if they did surrender? he wondered. Would the Israelites kill them all anyway, demolishing their gods and altars and temples along with them?

For days he kept to himself, rubbing his chin whiskers, and thinking. At night he lay awake, staring into the darkness. Gibeon perched atop a hill, only about six miles from Ai. Surely Joshua would attack it next. *I must come up with a plan!* he thought.

Then one night as he lay staring at nothing, an idea popped into his mind—a plan so tricky, so clever, so foolproof, that he laughed right out loud. "I just can't wait till morning!" he chortled.

As the faint fingers of dawn touched rooftops, walls, and vineyards with an eerie glow, he summoned the city officials.

Hastily seating themselves on stone benches at the city gate, they gazed curiously at their leader. Never before had they seen him so excited. He leaned forward, his tired eyes lit with glee at the daring of his own idea.

"I have a plan!" he exclaimed. "We cannot defend our-selves against the Israelites and their God. And just surren-dering to them will not save our lives, for they have been commanded to wipe out all the Baal-worshiping people in Canaan.

"But—" he paused dramatically, "I believe we can trick them into letting us live!"

"How?" his elders chorused, caught up in their leader's en-thusiasm. In hushed, secretive tones he revealed his scheme.

During the next few days the citizens of Gibeon gath-ered goatskin wine bags, the oldest they could find, and brought them to an excited group of women. The women grabbed them, deliberately tearing holes in them, laughing gleefully at the sheer foolishness of their own actions.

Then they bent over the newly ripped holes and tied them up again. And all the while they laughed until their sides hurt. They couldn't remember when they'd performed a sillier task.

Another strange thing was happening in the town of Gibeon. Their ruler had ordered, "Save your bread, the kind used for traveling. And let it get moldy!" So each fam-ily collected rings of half-baked bread dough. It molded quickly, and soon Gibeon seemed to overflow with stacks of moldy bread.

Next the Gibeonite leader told them, "Bring your worn-out sandals, the ones with holes and patches and worn straps, to the gate where an official will collect them. And bring your oldest, worn-out clothes, too!"

Finally one morning the commander's men collected all the tied-up wineskins, the moldy bread, the worn-out san-dals, and the threadbare clothes. Talking excitedly among themselves, they disappeared into a room.

When they came back out, the townspeople stared as some of their wealthiest men flapped around in rags and worn-out sandals. Some of their fussiest eaters clutched moldy bread. Everyone bunch carried a worn-out wineskin. But each had a big grin on his face as he waved an exaggerated goodbye to friends and family.

The people doubled over with laughter as they watched the men throw worn saddlebags over their donkeys and shuffle away. Those Israelites would soon learn how smart the people of Gibeon were!

A few hours later, at the Israelite camp at Gilgal, Joshua spotted a small group of travelers headed his way. He looked at them carefully. Who were they? Where had they come from? And what did they want?

The leader of the strangers stumbled up to Joshua, limping as if his feet were sore. Joshua noted his rags and worn-out sandals. Scanning the group, he noticed their tattered clothes, patched-up wineskins, and moldy bread poking out of the donkeys' worn saddlebags. Strangely, though, the donkeys did not seem tired at all.

What's going on here? he wondered.

The visitor cleared his throat while his eyes shifted from Joshua's forehead to his chin, to his ears, to his shoulders, never quite looking him in the eye. "We have come from a distant land to ask for a peace treaty with you," he began.

Several leaders of the tribes of Israel had gathered around Joshua. "How do we know you're from a distant land?" they asked. "Perhaps you live nearby, and if you do, we can't make a treaty with you."

At this point Joshua forgot to do something important. He failed to ask God to help him make the right decision. Instead he listened as the men said smoothly, "We are your servants. Come, now, make a treaty with us. We have heard of your God, and we've come a long way to make peace with the people who serve such a powerful God.

"When we left home our bread was fresh and warm from the oven. Now look at it. We've worn out our clothes and sandals through long, hard travel. Our wineskins were new, but they have burst on the way and we've had to tie them up."

Joshua relaxed. The men had come because they had heard about God. They called themselves Israel's "servants." And anyone could see that they must have traveled a long way to reach Gilgal.

As leader of the Israelites, Joshua offered them food and drink. Then he promised in the name of the Lord never to harm them. Israel's leaders also swore before God to keep peace with the Gibeonites.

Solemnly bowing and thanking Joshua for his kindness, the men left. But as soon as they were out of sight and earshot of the camp, they burst into gales of laughter. "Oh, did we fool them! Did you see the face of the old leader? He believed everything we said!" They could hardly wait to get back to Gibeon to spread the news.

Just three days later Joshua heard something that shocked him so much he could hardly speak. The "travelers," the men with whom he had formed a peace treaty, lived just a short distance away! The Lord had told him not to sign any treaties with neighboring Canaanites, but now he had done it.

When he could calm down, he gathered an army and marched into Gibeon. The Gibeonites peeked out of their little windows at the Israelites. Would the invaders go back on their word and attack them?

But the Israelite soldiers shot no arrows and hurled no slingstones. "Why don't we attack?" some demanded.

Sadly Joshua answered, "We did wrong in making a treaty with these people, but it was made in the name of the Lord, and we must not take His name in vain by breaking our promise."

Then Joshua, in ringing tones, summoned the leader of the Gibeonites. Timidly, guiltily, the ruler approached Joshua and looked into his blazing eyes. Somehow he didn't feel as smart and proud as he had a little while before. *Will the Israelites break their word?* he wondered. *Just how impor-*

tant to them is this God they serve? Is He important enough for them to keep their promise? Or will they simply forget the treaty and kill us?

Joshua answered his unspoken questions. "The God of Israel keeps His promises, and we will keep ours. But as you have proclaimed yourselves to be our servants, you will, indeed, be our slaves. From this day forward a curse will be on you for your deception, and you will work for us, chopping wood and carrying water for God's people and for His sanctuary."

The commander of Gibeon hung his head. The God of Israel was fair. And His people did keep their promises.

✄ ✄ ✄

Just as the tape was ending, the children heard a loud *thump* from inside the old mansion. Jason looked up, startled. "What was that?" he whispered.

"I don't know," Maria replied, edging close to Stacey. "I thought the professor was gone."

Stacey crept toward the window, the other two children pressing up against her. "Maybe someone's trying to steal the professor's treasures."

Another *thump* rattled from inside. Someone, or something, was definitely within the dark confines of the old mansion.

⑦
Samuel's Dream

Thump! Rattle, Rattle. Bang!

Jason's eyes opened even wider. "I'm gettin' outta here," he called as he raced toward the steps leading down from the broad porch.

"Wait for me!" Maria shouted, hot on his heels.

Stacey paused by the front door. "Hey, you guys. Hold it!"

Jason skidded to a stop, and Maria plowed into him from behind. The two sprawled across the cool leaves and uncut grasses, ending up in rumpled piles at the base of the tall oak.

A smile tugging at the corners of her mouth, Stacey said, "How many burglars whistle 'Jesus Loves Me' as they steal stuff?"

"What?" the other two chorused. "Someone's in the mansion whistling 'Jesus Loves Me'?"

Stacey listened then nodded. "Yup. Humming, too."

The children gathered at the front door and knocked loudly. The whistling stopped.

Soon the door creaked open, revealing the grinning face of Professor Appleby. "Well, hello. You're a little late, aren't you?"

Maria lifted her hand. "No. We—"

"Doesn't matter," the old man smiled. "Come on in, and I'll get some tapes ready."

"But—"

"The cassettes arrived about two weeks ago." The man paused. "Or was it before that? Never mind. You'll enjoy them anyway."

The children looked at each other and shrugged. No use trying to explain to the professor that they'd been there on the porch listening to a tape for the last half hour. And no use asking how he got back into the house without them seeing. The important thing was that they now had more tapes. That was all that really mattered.

Jason jogged over and retrieved the recorder from the porch table and hurried inside.

"Now," Professor Appleby said once everyone had settled by the fireplace, "let's hear what Maggie B has for us today."

This time, instead of wind noises, or the slap of oars, or the chirp of crickets, the children heard a train whistle, long and loud. When it faded away, only the rumble of rails and the creak of leather seats reverberated from the recorder. Then Maggie B's rich voice began to speak.

⚝ ⚝ ⚝

Hannah lay wide awake, staring into the darkness. She dreaded tomorrow when once again their little family would travel to Shiloh, where they'd offer sacrifices to God. Her husband, Elkanah, tried his best to keep it a happy occasion, but Penninah, his second wife, always made Hannah miserable.

Every year Penninah's boasting of her own little band of healthy children hurt Hannah more and more.

"O God," Hannah prayed as hot tears slid down her cheeks, "why have You not blessed me with children? Why have You not given me even one son?"

In the morning she hurried about her work, wrapping cheese and bread in a cloth, filling wineskins, pausing to pop a morsel of bread into the mouth of one of Penninah's children. She tried with all her might to be cheerful, to hide her sadness, but every now and then a big sigh escaped her lips.

Penninah's sharp eyes missed nothing. "My, but you're the gloomy one!" she exclaimed, her plump hands resting on her ample hips. "Now, I wonder what you've got to be so glum about . . . Couldn't be that another year has gone by and you still don't have a son, could it?

"Tell me, Hannah, what really bothers you most? Is it that

you're afraid Elkanah will love me more than you because I have borne him children? Or is it that everyone in the village knows God has cursed you, or—" With a cry Hannah fled, no longer able to stand Penninah's cruel tongue.

On the way to Shiloh, Hannah shuffled along, her gaze on the dusty ground. Elkanah cast worried looks in her direction, frequently riding his donkey close enough so that he could whisper, "What's wrong?" But Hannah only shook her head, not trusting herself to speak.

Finally Elkanah decided to take Hannah's mind off her troubles by talking to her. His voice rambled on and on, but Hannah hardly heard him. Then something he said caught her attention.

". . . and with such sons as Eli has, Hophni and Phinehas, serving in the tabernacle, I expect that soon the Lord will raise up another leader of Israel. Eli, the high priest, is a good man, but he does not control his sons, and they're a disgrace to the Lord."

Hannah's mind wandered off again with the word "sons." *Dear God,* she prayed once more, *why is there no son for me? If You were to give me a child, I would raise him to love and serve You . . .*

Coming over a ridge, they spotted the tabernacle—the same tabernacle the priests had carried through the Sinai wilderness. Crowds gathered in the courtyard as men of Israel, one by one, laid their slain animals on the altar.

At last Elkanah completed his sacrifice, and the whole family sat down to eat together, adding the leftover meat from their offering to their lunch. Elkanah's face beamed with happiness as he prayed, thanking God for the food and for His goodness. Then with a flourish he cut off portions of the meat and served them.

The children's eyes sparkled as they saw the big servings coming their way. People did not get meat often. Proudly lifting her chin, Penninah darted a superior look at Hannah as Elkanah gave her a generous portion. Then he served Hannah—a serving so big that everyone stared in shocked silence.

Penninah's face reddened with anger and she glared at Hannah. Hannah felt a lump in her throat. She knew Elkanah meant well, but why did he have to single her out? It just made his other wife more spiteful than ever. Glancing up, she saw Penninah's eyes on her.

Then, making sure Elkanah didn't see her, Penninah quickly, softly, clapped her hands together in a gesture of contempt. Hannah flushed. The action said, more plainly than words, *You're a nobody. You're a nothing. You can't even bear your husband one son. What good are you, anyway? You ought to crawl away and die.*

Feeling sick, Hannah laid down her food. Tears swam in her eyes. Stumbling away from the feast, she headed toward the tabernacle. But Elkanah, his dark eyes round with concern, caught up with her. "What's wrong?" he asked. "Why aren't you eating?"

Hannah merely shook her head. Finally she choked, "I don't want extra portions of food. I want a son, Elkanah. *I want a son!*"

Elkanah hardly knew what to say. Awkwardly he touched her arm. "But am I not a good husband to you? Could I treat you any better if you had 10 sons?"

She felt a helpless, hopeless feeling sweep over her. He didn't understand. Good as he was, he just didn't understand.

Through trembling lips she whispered, "Please, I'd like to be alone," and she stumbled, blinded by tears, toward the tabernacle.

Eli, the high priest, sat at the entrance. He watched, curious, as Hannah staggered toward him, then sank to her knees at the foot of the altar in the courtyard.

Silently she began to pray. Rocking back and forth, eyes squeezed shut, lips moving, she begged God for a son. She told Him all about her trials with Penninah and her great sorrow. Finally she vowed, *If You will only remember me in my misery, O Lord, and give me a son, I will give him to You all the days of his life. In fact, I will dedicate Him to you as a Nazirite, and no razor will ever touch a hair on his head.*

The more Eli watched, the more disturbed he became. *This woman must be drunk,* he thought. *Imagine coming into God's tabernacle in such a condition!*

Jumping to his feet, he approached her. "Woman," he asked sternly, "must you come here drunk? Get rid of your wine!"

Hannah gasped in astonishment as she raised her tear-streaked face to the high priest. "Oh, my lord," she exclaimed, "I'm not drunk! But I am deeply troubled, and have been pouring out my grief to God."

Stumbling over her words, Hannah told him of her longing, and of her vow. Eli's eyes softened as he listened. *This woman is willing to do whatever God requires, even if it means giving Him her son,* he marveled.

Kindly, he answered, "Go in peace, and may the God of Israel grant what you have asked of Him."

Suddenly Hannah felt happy. "Oh, thank you!" she murmured, then with light steps she hurried back to her family. And ignoring Penninah's astonished stares and Elkanah's look of pleased bewilderment, she sat down to eat.

A year later Hannah lay very still in the half darkness just before dawn. Today the family would again go to Shiloh to offer sacrifices. But this time she would stay home. Carefully shifting her position, she bent to kiss her baby's soft cheek as he snuggled in the curve of her arm.

The infant blinked, squinted, and yawned. Hannah laughed softly. "Samuel," she murmured, "do you know why we named you that? It is because your name means that I asked the Lord for you and He heard what I asked. You are God's answer to my prayer, my little son. But you are not really mine, for I promised you to God."

Suddenly Samuel opened his big, dark eyes and focused on his mother's face. Hannah could have sworn that he understood her every word. A smile on her lips, she cuddled him and dreamed of what Samuel might some day do for God.

But God had His dreams too. And His dreams for Samuel were even bigger than Hannah's.

✕ ✕ ✕

"What happens next? What happens next?" the children urged as Professor Appleby popped the cassette out.

"Hang on," he chuckled as he reached for another one. "Patience is a virtue. All things come to those who wait. A stitch in time saves nine." The old man paused. "No, wait. That last one doesn't fit." He looked over at his three visitors. "But it's a good saying anyhow."

With a grin he slipped the next cassette into the machine. Again the rattle of train wheels filled the room. Then Maggie B took up the story where she had left off.

✕ ✕ ✕

Samuel clung tightly to his mother's neck as she whirled him around and around the room. Squealing with laughter, he gasped, "Do it again! Do it again!"

Just then Elkanah stepped through the door. A smile lit his eyes as he looked first at Hannah, then at Samuel, their little gift from God. *What a change in Hannah!* he thought. *I remember when her face held only sadness. Now she simply glows with happiness.*

And Samuel—how he had grown! Elkanah beamed with pride. *Had there ever been such a good little boy as Samuel?* he asked himself. *No, never.*

Soon Hannah lay the child down for a nap. Then she turned to her husband. "Come outside with me," she suggested. Smiling his agreement, Elkanah led the way.

Summer's heat, heavy and golden, rippled across the hilltop where their home nestled among a cluster of stone houses like their own. After slowly making their way to a spreading fig tree, they sat in its welcome shade.

Hannah turned to Elkanah. "It's time, my husband," she said softly, huskily. Elkanah caught his breath. His wife had told him of her promise to give their son to God, to serve the high priest at the tabernacle, but they had not discussed it for some time.

Now as he looked into her eyes, brimming with sadness, he felt suddenly lonely and empty at the thought of parting with Samuel. *He's so little!* he thought. *How will we ever get along without him?* For a fleeting instant he thought of refusing to let Samuel go. As the head of the household, he could free his wife from her vow.

But if Hannah could trust God to take care of their son, so could he. With an effort he kept his voice matter-of-fact. "Yes," he answered. "The time has come to take Samuel to the tabernacle."

Little Samuel clung tightly to his mother's hand as he looked up at the enormous bulk of Eli, the white-bearded high priest. He understood snatches of the conversation. "This is the child God gave me," he heard his mother telling the man.

Eli's eyes widened with surprise and respect. In all his many years he had never seen anyone make such a sacrifice. He still remembered the day this woman had tearfully begged the Lord for a son. Now she was keeping her promise to give him back to God.

Then Hannah was kneeling in front of Samuel, hugging him, whispering last-minute instructions in his tiny ear, reminding him to help Eli and always to obey God and to serve Him. At last she stood, wiping her wet face with her sleeve. "I'll be back!" she promised. "I'll come back often, and every year I'll bring you a new coat."

Eli watched Samuel as the child's parents turned and walked away from their little boy. Would the boy scream and cry and try to run after them? No one could blame him if he did.

But Samuel stood by Eli, just as his mother had told him to. He whimpered softly, while big tears rolled down his chubby cheeks. Samuel didn't fully understand what was happening, but he remembered his mother telling him, "You're God's little boy. You're special. You will work for Him and do whatever He wants you to do. And Eli will take care of you."

Suddenly Eli felt a little hand slip into his, and he glanced down to see Samuel's big dark eyes, bright with tears, gazing up at him. "What do you want me to do for you?" the child whispered.

As the months rolled by, Eli began to wonder how he had ever managed without Samuel. He was always helping. The women who served at the sanctuary loved him and took care of him.

Whether cleaning up after services or searching for

something Eli's fading eyesight could not find, the child did his best. Whenever he felt homesick or unhappy, he would tell himself, "I'm God's little boy, and He is here with me in this special place."

As time passed, Samuel outgrew his litle boy chubbiness and developed into a strong and sturdy lad. And each time his parents came to offer the yearly sacrifice, his mother brought him a bigger coat.

But the older he grew, the more he noticed that Eli's sons, in spite of being priests, were wicked men. They stole meat offered for sacrifices, disobeyed God's rules, and treated the women badly.

Eli, well aware of his sons' actions, sighed and shook his head, but did nothing to stop their wicked ways. Samuel talked to no one except God about the things that troubled him. "Help me never to act like that, and always to honor You," he prayed.

One night Samuel rested on his mat near the holy place. The soft glow of the golden lamp cast warm, comforting shadows. His eyelids grew heavy, but suddenly he sprang to his feet as a voice said his name. *Eli needs something!* he thought as he ran to him.

"What is it, Eli?" he asked anxiously, staring down at the old man. The priest jerked awake and rubbed his eyes. "Huh? What?"

"You called me, sir. What did you want?"

"I—I didn't call you. Go back to bed."

Puzzled, Samuel padded back to his mat. He felt sure Eli had summoned him.

Just as he felt himself getting sleepy once more, a voice, loud and distinct, repeated, "Samuel!"

Samuel jumped up and ran to the old priest's resting place. "What is it, Eli? I heard you say my name."

Now what's the matter with that boy tonight? Eli asked himself, but he answered patiently, "I didn't call you, son. Now go on back to bed."

More puzzled than ever, the boy once more lay down on his mat. But this time he had hardly wrapped his cloak around him when he heard that voice again. "Samuel! Samuel!"

Hurrying to the high priest, he asked, "What do you need, sir? I'm sure I heard you calling me."

Eli raised himself on one elbow and peered into Samuel's face, so young, so concerned, so eager to help. And then he knew. For many years God had not talked directly to any of His people, but He was speaking now—to Samuel.

In a voice full of wonder, he told him, "Go and lie down, and if you hear your name again, say, 'Speak, Lord, for Your servant hears.'"

The boy's eyes grew round and his heart pounded with excitement. Was it possible? Could he have heard the voice of God speaking to him?

He lay on his mat once more, hardly breathing. Then he heard it. "Samuel!"

Staring into the darkness, he answered in a trembling voice, "Speak, for Your servant hears."

Then God talked to Samuel. He told him all about His plans, and He told him some bad news. "Eli's sons have sinned against Me," God said. "And Eli has ignored My warnings to correct them. Because they will not repent, they will not let Me forgive them. Soon I will have to end their wickedness."

Long after God had stopped speaking, Samuel lay in the darkness, his mind repeating again and again every word God had spoken. So many feelings churned inside him that he couldn't sleep. He could hardly believe that God had talked to him. And he felt almost sick at the thought of having to tell Eli that God was about to punish him and his sons.

In the morning he avoided Eli, keeping busy with opening up the tabernacle and doing one little chore after another. Finally the high priest caught up with him.

"What did God say to you last night?" Eli asked.

Samuel gulped as he glanced at his white-bearded face with the faded gray eyes. How could he hurt this kind old man? But he remembered his mother's words, "You're God's special boy," and he knew he must tell the truth.

So, lifting his chin, he looked squarely into Eli's eyes and repeated God's message.

The priest sat down heavily, his head in his hands. But when at last he raised his face to Samuel, he smiled bravely.

"God is fair," he murmured softly. "And He has chosen you, Samuel, to be Israel's next great leader."

Soon word spread throughout Israel, from north to south, that God had selected a new leader, the young Samuel. Marketplaces and workshops buzzed with the news. Children everywhere began to wonder if perhaps God had something special for them to do too.

But one person was not surprised. One person had known all along that Samuel was God's special boy who would one day be His special man. And that person was Hannah, whom God now honored with three more sons and two daughters.

✕ ✕ ✕

"Wow," Jason breathed as the tape ended. "I've never had any voice call to me while I was sleeping. I'd be kinda scared."

"Not if the voice belonged to God," Professor Appleby said softly.

The children rose and stretched their arms and legs. "Thanks, Professor," they said, making their way out into the entryway and then to the front door. "We sure like Maggie B's stories. How 'bout tomorrow?" They paused a moment. "But we don't want you to get tired of us hangin' around every afternoon."

"Nonsense," the old man laughed. "You're welcome here anytime. I'll look forward to your visit."

Stacey, Maria, and Jason turned to leave. "Oh, one more

thing," the professor called after them. "Try not to be late. There's something I want to show you when the box comes."

Maria lifted her hand and pointed toward the table resting at the far end of the porch. "But we—"

"See you tomorrow," the old man called with a wave.

Maria sighed and continued walking down the path into the forest. Professor Appleby was one strange person, that was for sure. But he was a kind man who loved to share his sister's stories with them. Maybe strange wasn't so bad after all.

STEP BY STEP

Samuel recognized it. Can you? Connect the letters that will help you reach the finish in just nine moves. Use each chosen letter and pathway only once. What do the letters spell?

Answer: __ __ __ __ __ __ __ __ __

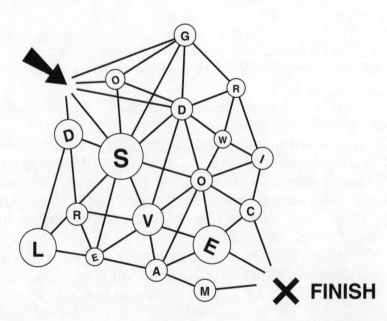

⑧
Philistines Take the Ark

"**G**uess what this is?" Professor Appleby called out as he lifted a carefully wrapped object from the newly arrived box in his front room.

"A lamp?" Maria ventured.

"A potted plant?" Stacey asked.

"A shrunken head from Africa," Jason joined in.

"Yuck!" Maria gasped. "Don't listen to him, Professor. He's got a wild imagination."

The old man laughed. "No, it's not a lamp or plant, and certainly not a shrunken head." He pulled a glass container from the brown wrapping paper. "It's a water pitcher, for drinking."

The children pressed in to admire the smooth contours of the mysterious object. It had a big, round middle and a skinny neck. A small, looped handle graced one side, and a curving spout jutted from the other.

"Come, I'll show you how it works," Professor Appleby said. "It's called an *ibreek*, and it's meant to keep water cool in the hot desert. Archaeologists drink from them all the time."

The group moved quickly into the cluttered kitchen just off the hallway. At the sink the old man filled the container with water from the faucet, then held the object slightly above his head.

"See, you tip it like so, and the water will come running out of the spout right into your mouth." The children watched as a stream of water arched from the little spout and struck the professor directly on the nose.

The old man coughed and sputtered. "Guess I'm not too good at drinking Middle East style. I'd better practice while you listen to the tape. Deal?"

Maria and Jason nodded between giggles and headed for the den. Stacey led the group into the large, cheery room and fitted a new tape into the machine. The familiar rattle of railroad cars drifted in the cool air. Maggie B had recorded another Bible story on her train trip, perhaps somewhere along the Nile between Cairo and Luxor.

⚔ ⚔ ⚔

Eli shifted his heavy body on the backless stool. His blind old eyes strained uselessly to see down the road in the direction of Ebenezer, where the Israelite army camped.

A feeling of dread, a terrible sense of foreboding, gripped him like cold, hard bands of bronze. Ever since Samuel had prophesied against his family, the high priest had not had a moment's peace.

But nothing had changed. His sons, Hophni and

Phinehas, continued their wicked ways. Samuel had grown into manhood, and God continued to talk to him. Many in Israel, watching the behavior of the priests, lost respect for their own religion and even for God Himself.

Now—again—the Philistines had attacked. Hophni and Phinehas had hurried to join the men, young and old, in Israel's army. Every day they were away, Eli sat on his stool near the tabernacle, waiting for word from the battlefront.

Excitement ran high in the camp of the Israelite army. Full of rash self-confidence, they bragged to each other about what they would do to those Philistines.

"We'll teach them a lesson this time!" they crowed. "They think they're pretty smart camping at Aphek, where they're protected from the north by swamps and springs, but look at us! We're blocking their only route over this ridge into the hill country they're trying to take away from us." Everyone laughed and nodded, jabbing and thrusting at imaginary Philistines with their bronze swords or makeshift weapons.

But not one soldier remembered that God had not given them instructions for the battle. And not one soldier remembered to ask Him to be with them.

Then the Philistines attacked. Waves of battle wagons bore down on the Israelites so fast that they hardly had time to lift their swords or shoot an arrow. Horses overran them as thousands of iron-tipped spears rained down upon them. And before the Israelites could recover, Philistine foot soldiers, wielding deadly iron swords, swarmed over them, slashing and stabbing. As bronze met iron, the Israelite swords cracked, shattered, or separated from the handle. Broken blades sailed into the air, then tumbled to the ground, leaving Israelite soldiers empty-handed and helpless. Amid the confusion of dust and falling bodies and cries of the wounded, an Israelite general bellowed, "Retreat, retreat!"

Back at camp, the Israelite army took stock of its

losses. Four thousand dead. The remaining soldiers stared at each other with panic-stricken faces. The same thought was in everyone's mind. The next attack could be a complete slaughter.

"What are we going to do? What are we going to do?" The question echoed from mouth to mouth. "Why did the Lord bring defeat upon us from the Philistines?"

Then someone came up with an idea. "Let's get the ark and take it into battle with us!" Everyone cheered.

"Why didn't we think of that before?" someone said.

But God was most unhappy. Was this what His people thought of Him, that He was a good-luck charm they could carry around with them? That they could force Him to do their will?

God felt as if His heart would break. His people no longer worshiped only Him. Nor did they ask for His help or His counsel. Again and again He had won battles and worked miracles for them. But instead of praising Him and loving Him, they turned their backs and bowed down to idols. And where was their respect for the ark of the covenant, the sacred symbol of His presence?

But the soldiers thought it was a wonderful idea to bring the ark to the battlefield. Joyfully a group of men ran as fast as they could up the mountain trail toward Shiloh.

Eli heard footsteps approaching, followed by loud voices and boisterous laughter. His heart nearly stopped when the footsteps entered the sanctuary. "Wha—what's going on there?" he called, wishing he could see.

"Never mind, old man!" someone rudely replied. Then Eli sensed them leaving the sanctuary. Their footsteps were slower and their voices breathless, as if perhaps they were carrying something heavy.

"What are you doing?" he demanded. "Are you taking something from the tabernacle?"

"Don't worry, we'll bring it back!" And they left.

Eli's heart pounded furiously as he suddenly realized

what they were doing. The ark! They must have taken God's holy ark of the covenant with them. Rocking back and forth on his stool, he muttered to himself. "It's happening. O God, I've failed You so. Why did I . . . my sons . . . priesthood taken away from my family, and now . . . oh, what next?"

As the soldiers carrying the ark approached their camp, a great shout went up—a cheer, a warcry. About two miles to the west, in their camp at Aphek, the Philistines also heard the shout.

"What is it?" they asked each other.

A scout raced, breathless, into camp. "The Israelites," he panted, "have their God with them!"

"What do you mean?" their commander thundered.

"The box, the chest they call the ark of the covenant. Their God is in it!" the scout stammered.

Silence, thick with superstition, fell on the Philistines. At last someone gulped, "We're done for! Their God is the same one who brought all those plagues on the Egyptians. We don't have a chance. They'll capture us and make us slaves."

But their commander drew himself to his full height and roared, "Then we will fight as we've never fought before. If we die, we'll die fighting!" And with a fierce war cry of their own, the Philistine army rushed toward the oncoming Israelites.

Hophni and Phinehas balanced the ark between them, while two other men held it in the rear. With their free hands they waved their swords. Grinning with foolish excitement, they plunged into the battle.

Suddenly they were face-to-face with the wild-eyed Philistines. Desperately the Philistine soldiers screamed and thrust with their heavy, black, but perfectly balanced swords. Hophni and Phinehas sank lifeless to the ground.

The other two dropped the ark and tried to escape, but in vain. All around the ark Israelite soldiers fell.

The Philistines, suddenly aware that they were winning

the battle, fought with fresh strength and deadly courage. At last, as more and more Israelites fled for their lives, the Philistines hoisted God's holy ark to their shoulders, and rushed victoriously back to camp.

Eli, sitting, waiting, heard the mingling of a great shout and a mournful roar. "What's happening? What's happening?" he cried. At last a runner, his clothes torn and with dirt on his head as a sign of mourning, staggered up to him.

"I—I've just come from the battle!" he panted.

The old priest's heart lurched with fear. "Tell me, my son—what happened?"

"Israel fled from the Philistines. We suffered a terrible defeat. Thousands must have been killed." Eli moaned softly.

"Your sons, Hophni and Phinehas, are dead." A groan escaped the high priest's lips.

"And the ark of God has been captured." Eli cried out in dreadful anguish. Then his massive body, 98 years old, toppled backward from the stool. The runner dashed forward to help him, but it was too late. Eli had broken his neck and died.

Nearby, his daughter-in-law, the wife of Phinehas, rested on her mat, waiting to give birth. Shocked and sorrowful, she heard the message brought by the refugee from battle, and then the great commotion as people discovered that their high priest had died.

The loss of her husband, her father-in-law, and above all, the news that the symbol of God's presence now rested in pagan hands, struck her like a blow. Then the baby came, but as it breathed its first gasps of air, Phinehas' wife was breathing her last.

The women with her tried to revive her. "You have a son!" they exclaimed. "You have something to live for!" But the dying woman only whispered, "Name him Ichabod, 'no glory,' for the glory of God has indeed departed from Israel!"

The sad news reached Ramah, where the prophet Samuel now lived. He bowed his head in sorrow. God's message, given to him when he was a little boy, had at last been fulfilled.

✗ ✗ ✗

"That's sad," Jason said softly as Maggie B's voice faded. "I wonder if they ever got their ark back."

"Oh yes," Professor Appleby called from the doorway. "But that's another story for another day." The old man smiled. "Before you go, I want you to see how well I can drink from this *ibreek* now." He hoisted the pitcher high above his head. "Watch this. You're supposed to catch the water in your mouth without closing it to swallow. It's hard."

As before, a steady stream of water poured from the odd-shaped jar and splashed down the already soaked front of the old man. Jason and Maria laughed long and loud, enjoying the professor's renewed attempts to drink from the jug.

Stacey didn't laugh, however. She seemed almost embarrassed by the old man's antics. "Don't do that," she called out nervously. "You're making a mess of yourself. Just don't do it anymore." Professor Appleby lowered the jar. "It's OK," he said. "I'll dry out in time. I just—"

"We've got to go now," she interrupted, running from the room. "Come on, you guys. It's almost suppertime."

The other two children looked at each other and shrugged. It was getting a little late.

With a smile and wave they ran after their companion. The old man stood in the doorway watching them go, concern shadowing his face. "I just wanted to show you how it's done," he said to no one. "I just wanted to hear you laugh."

BIBLE PLACES

In the Bible Word Digs your assignment is to excavate the words hidden in the strata of letters in this block that is your responsibility to unearth. The hidden words may be located vertically, horizontally, or diagonally. So get out your archaeological digging tools and have a little fun.

```
U  A  I  R  I  J  Y  X  C  M  M  V
R  F  D  A  U  E  H  S  O  D  O  M
Q  J  A  O  L  R  N  E  Y  Y  G  C
Z  G  G  Z  N  I  H  B  O  W  Q  Y
S  G  R  V  W  C  C  E  H  C  O  J
H  I  E  A  P  H  G  N  Z  X  E  B
I  B  G  Z  D  O  U  E  B  X  F  J
L  E  Y  P  J  R  F  Z  A  E  K  Y
O  O  P  I  T  I  A  E  O  R  I  V
H  N  T  K  H  U  Y  R  M  M  R  J
G  O  M  O  R  R  A  H  V  A  G  Z
I  R  T  F  R  G  N  L  P  M  R  P
```

WORD LIST

EBENEZER	COMORRAH	MOAB	ZOAR
EGYPT	JERICHO	SHILOH	
GIBEON	MAMRE	SODOM	

BIBLE PEOPLE

```
S A M U E L V A U H S O J A W
D N G T O R E U B E N M V Y M
O R V H O A R A H P E D W A G
R A N A K L E D N L Q I I B O
E H Z H H J F L I U J U R R V
H A E N A A P H T A N H P A Z
Q B Y K N R N V O P Q P X H K
B O C A J Y D N J J O D O A I
S I M E O N H Z I T Z V C M C
M A G I I U M A I N E Z H V H
S A R A H N H P N A E J P S A
A S E N A T H O F N Y P E U B
T O L L W A U P F J A S S O
W M W Y R A M A O C K H O E D
B N I M M A N E B H L U J J A
```

WORD LIST

ABRAHAM	JACOB	PHARAOH
ASENATH	JESUS	POTIPHAR
BENAMMI	JOSEPH	RAHAB
ELI	JOSHUA	REUBEN
ELKANA	LOT	SAMUEL
HANNAH	MAGI	SARAH
HEROD	MARY	SIMEON
HOPHNI	NUN	ZAPHNATHPAANEAH
ICHABOD	PENINNAH	

⑨
Birth of Jesus

There's something strange going on around here," Jason whispered as he and Maria hurried a few paces behind Stacey. The afternoon was cool, almost cold. Winter was offering the land a sneak preview of things to come.

"You mean Stacey and Professor Appleby?" Maria questioned.

"Yeah. She doesn't seem surprised by his funny ways. Nor does she laugh much when he says something really crazy. And her mom told mine that it was safe for us to visit him. I don't know what's going on. It's almost as if Stacey knows him from somewhere."

"What're you guys whispering about?" the girl in the lead turned and called over her shoulder.

"Oh, nothing," Jason stammered. "Just talking about the professor and how weird he is."

"He's not weird!" Stacey stopped and spun around. "I mean, he's a little strange sometimes, but—"

"Sometimes?" Maria giggled.

The girl with the blond hair clenched her fists. "Don't talk bad about the professor. He's a nice man, and we should be glad he's sharing those tapes with us."

Maria blinked. "Hey, I didn't say anything *bad* about him. I like the professor. He's fun. But he is a little different than most people, and you can't say he isn't."

Stacey turned quickly and continued walking up the long forest path leading to the old mansion. Jason glanced over at Maria and shrugged.

"Hi, kids," the old man called from the porch as the three entered the clearing. "Whatta ya think?"

The visitors stopped dead in their tracks. Their friend was dressed head to toe in the weirdest looking outfit they'd ever seen. He wore a bright-red cloth fastened to his head with a black rope. Cream-colored folds of material cascaded from his shoulders and flowed to sandal-covered feet. At his waist another rope held the gown tightly about his middle.

"Today I'm an Arab," the old man said proudly. "Isn't it great? Maggie B sent it. She remembered my size and everything. This is what people wear in the country she's visiting right now."

Stacey stepped forward. "You look silly," she blurted. "You shouldn't wear that. People will think you're a strange, weird old man."

Professor Appleby's mouth dropped open. "Oh, I'm sorry, Stacey," he said. "I didn't mean to embarrass you. I just thought you would like to see what—"

The girl hid her face in her hands. "Why can't you be like other people? Why can't you be like a normal grandfather?"

Jason's and Maria's eyes widened. "Grandfather?" they gasped. "Professor Appleby is your grandfather?"

"Yes," the girl sobbed. "I didn't want you to know. I didn't want anyone to know."

"Why?" Maria asked, her face puzzled. "He's a nice man. Anyone would be proud to have him—"

"But you said he was weird and strange," Stacey interrupted. "Other kids at school say the same thing. They say he's just a silly old man living in a run-down house in the woods. I've heard 'em talk. I know what they say."

The cool afternoon breeze whispered past the porch and sang a low melody in the branches of the oak. Professor Appleby stood on the steps watching the sobbing girl, his eyes filled with love and understanding. But a tiny flicker of hurt shone there too.

"Stacey," he said softly. "I know I'm kinda strange, living out here like I do. But this was my father's house. It's all I have. I can't go anywhere else. And all the things I've collected, all the treasures Maggie B has sent, are important to me. They're like old friends. I'd be unhappy without them."

His granddaughter looked up at him. "I do love you, Grandfather. Really. It just hurts me when people say those things, and laugh at you. And . . . I don't want them to think I'm crazy too."

Maria stepped forward. "Let 'em," she said. "Let 'em think whatever they want. We know better. We know the professor is a nice man. Jason and me, we're sorry about what we said in the past."

"Yeah," Jason added. "Who cares what other people think? When you know the truth, it doesn't matter anymore."

Stacey wiped tears from her face with the back of her hand. "I'm sorry, Grandfather. I guess . . . I guess I was being a little selfish. Will you forgive me?"

The old man wrapped the girl in his arms. "Of course I will. I just want you to be my friend. I know I may seem weird, but that's the way the good Lord made me. He must've figured this world needed a crazy professor like me."

She smiled, blinking the remaining tears away. "I need you too."

"And don't forget us," Jason and Maria chimed in. "We've never had a friend like you before."

"Speaking of friends," the professor said as if suddenly remembering something important, "would you like to hear the mysterious story of how God became the best friend this world has ever seen?"

"*The tapes!*" the children shouted. "*To the tapes!*"

They hurried into the mansion and settled themselves in the den. Professor Appleby slipped the first cassette into the machine. This time the storyteller must have been out in a pasture somewhere, because in the background they could hear the sound of sheep bleating. Then the voice of Maggie B filled the room.

✗ ✗ ✗

Joseph stared at Mary, the blood pounding in his ears,

his face flaming. What was this she was telling him? She was going to have a baby? And an angel had come to tell her so?

Sick with confusion, he turned away. His Mary. His sweet, innocent Mary, whom he had vowed to wed. How could she betray him like this, and how could she lie about it?

Slowly he faced her again. Her dark eyes held tears, but strangely, not a trace of guilt. Knowing and trusting her as he did, he was almost tempted to believe her wild story. But common sense stepped in. No decent woman got pregnant before the marriage feast. It was a disgrace, and he would have to divorce her.

Clearing his throat, feeling as if he might strangle on the words, he said, "You must realize that I will have to end the betrothal. But I will make no public announcement. I'll take care of everything as quietly as I can to save you embarrassment."

He paused. The tears in her eyes now flowed freely down her smooth young cheeks. Swallowing a big lump in his throat, he shuffled his feet. Then, unable to think of anything else to say, he walked stiffly away.

Mary headed toward home, stumbling and crying. But she hadn't gone far when she stopped and looked up at the blue sky. "Dear God," she murmured, wiping her tears, "You did send your angel to me! The baby inside me is Your special gift. And even if no one else in the whole world believes it, I still know it's true."

Lowering herself to sit on a grassy patch among the stones, in memory she saw again the angel Gabriel and heard his astonishing words.

"The Lord is with you, favored one!" She had started to tremble, confused and afraid.

Then in the kindest, gentlest voice, the angel had continued. "Don't be afraid, Mary, for you have found favor with God. Very soon now He will bless you with a baby boy, and you shall call Him Jesus.

"He will grow into greatness, and people will call Him the Son of the Most High God. The Lord will give Him the throne of his ancestor, David, and He will rule over the children of Jacob forever. In fact, His kingdom shall never end!"

Mary still trembled. Yet she believed every word the angel said, even though she could not understand how it would come about, or why God had chosen her for such an honor.

With complete trust she asked, "Can you explain how this will happen, since I'm still only betrothed?"

Gabriel's eyes sparkled with joy. "The Holy Spirit will come to you and overshadow you. And the baby born to you will be holy, the Son of God."

A smile touched Mary's lips as she sat lost in memory. Joseph might turn away from her. People might call her rude names. They might even make fun of her baby, born without a father. But no one could take away the angel's announcement.

That night Joseph tossed and turned, trying to sleep. He felt as if a thousand voices had stormed into his mind and started shouting at each other.

How could you doubt the words of Mary?
Don't be silly. Who could believe them?
She's never lied before.
That's right. But maybe she never had a reason to!
Joseph, she looked so sad when you walked away.
But what else could I do? What else?

At last he fell into a troubled sleep. And a dream chased away all the voices, for there, right beside him, stood the angel Gabriel. And the angel spoke in a warm, low voice. "Joseph, descendant of David, don't let your doubts keep you from marrying Mary. The child within her is of the Holy Spirit. She will have a Son, and you shall name Him Jesus, the Saviour, for He will save His people from their sins!

"You know the Scriptures, Joseph. Do you remember Isaiah's prophecy that says a virgin shall conceive, and bear a son, and He will be called Immanuel, God with us?

That prophecy is again being fulfilled right now. Mary is that virgin, and her son is the One promised to Adam and Eve, to Abraham, to the prophets, and to you!"

Joseph woke up so excited he couldn't go back to sleep. As soon as daylight struck, he bolted from his bed and raced through the little village of Nazareth to Mary's house.

"Mary!" he called as soon as she came outside. "Please forgive me! The angel came to me in a dream, and I was wrong, and I want to marry you right away!" He stopped, gasping for breath.

Half laughing, half crying, she rushed into his arms. But the tears in her deep-brown eyes were ones of happiness.

Soon Joseph took her to his home as his bride. Weeks and months passed. They settled into the busy life of the little town of Nazareth.

One day while Mary sat piecing together a new cloak for Joseph, he rushed into the room, his eyes wide and worried.

"What's wrong?" she asked, rising slowly, awkwardly to her feet. *I'm so big!* she thought. *This baby is going to be born soon.* But she couldn't think about that right now. Something was worrying her husband.

"I just heard—! The Roman emperor, Caesar Augustus, has decreed that the empire must be taxed. And every family has to travel to the place its ancestors came from to register and be counted."

"That means we'll have to go to Bethlehem!" Mary exclaimed, her face pale. But then she forced a smile. "I guess I'd better start packing."

Joseph smiled gratefully at her. He wouldn't have blamed her if she had stormed, "I can't go! It's almost time for my baby to be born! I can't take the chance of having it beside the road somewhere."

Yet he knew she was worried. And so was he.

On a bright fall morning when fluffy clouds swirled around the mountains now green from the rainy season, Joseph and Mary, along with dozens of other families, trudged toward Bethlehem.

Mary sat sideways on a gentle old donkey. Yet with every step the donkey took she lurched forward, then back, over and over again. Joseph, leading the animal, kept glancing back at her, anxious and worried.

"Are you all right?" he asked every few minutes.

"Of course!" Mary smiled, but she was worried too. On the fifth day of their travels, a sudden, sharp pain told her that the baby, her miracle baby, would be born before many more hours had passed.

At last she could hide her troubles no longer. "Joseph, will we reach Bethlehem soon? It—it's almost time!"

His hands shook. "We're almost there, Mary. Just over that ridge, see?"

Bethlehem sat high on a hilltop, a cluster of white-washed buildings bathed in the warm afternoon sunlight. Green fields, terraced like giant steps while groves of olive trees cast sun-dappled shadows along the paths.

But as they came closer, the peaceful scene vanished. Crowds of travelers jostled one another on the narrow road. And beggars—mostly children—swarmed over them with outstretched hands, demanding just one little coin.

Mary lowered her head while Joseph, ignoring the babble, plowed through the crowd. He had to find a place where he and Mary could stay, a place where Mary could give birth to her holy baby.

"Surely someone will have a room to rent," Joseph muttered to himself. Expecting the village's one inn to be full, he decided to try a private house. At the first one where he knocked, an old, bent woman peered out at him. "No more room!" she shrilled. "We're full."

Joseph could see that she told the truth. Donkeys crowded around her door, and from inside the house he could hear children crying—certainly not her own. People even crowded her flat roof.

"This place is too near the edge of town," he explained

to Mary with a confidence he did not feel. "Everyone probably stopped here first. But we'll find a place soon."

But they did not find room at the next house, or the next. Feeling more and more worried, Joseph kept on knocking. At every door he received the same answer. "Sorry. We're full. Everyone under the sun has come to town, you know. You should have arrived earlier."

Joseph bit his lip to keep from answering. *Come earlier? Over such a rough road with a donkey and a pregnant wife?*

He glanced at the sky. Soon it would be dark. Mary sat on the donkey, tight-lipped and white, her large eyes like two pools of pain. "I've got to find a place to stay!" Joseph suddenly shouted to the milling crowd, hoping someone, anyone, would listen. "My wife's going to have a baby—soon!"

An old man turned around. "Try the other side of town," he advised.

"Thank you!" Joseph replied while he urged the donkey to move faster. A groan escaped Mary's lips.

At last they reached the village's one inn. Joseph guessed he would have to try it after all. "I'll be right back!" he assured her, elbowing his way through the crowd into the dimly lit room where other travelers pleaded loudly, offering more money than they could afford, just for a space to put down their mats.

Raising his voice with the others, Joseph finally caught the innkeeper's attention. "Sir, my wife is about to give birth! We must have a place to stay."

The words, the tone of voice, the expression on Joseph's face, caught the sympathy of the big, sharp-featured innkeeper. But what could he do? Everyone wanted a place to stay, and he just didn't have any more room.

"I'd help if I could, but all my space is already taken. I've even got one family that—"

Joseph broke in impatiently, "How about the roof? Surely you have something!"

The innkeeper looked into Joseph's desperate eyes. The

thought darted through his mind, *I suppose they could have my room,* but he quickly brushed it aside. He couldn't start playing favorites here. Everyone had some emergency or another. Still . . .

As he followed Joseph's worried glance to the crowded courtyard, he saw Mary holding on grimly to the old gray donkey. "I'll tell you what," he blurted. "There are several caves in the hills just behind the inn. The local herdsmen use them for stables in the winter, you know, but you should be able to find one that's reasonably clean." Motioning to a child to lead the couple, he turned to the others who pulled at his clothes, begging for shelter.

Grateful by now for any place at all to stay, Joseph followed the child up a rocky path. Night had fallen, and stars twinkled in the velvet sky. At last they reached a spot where the darkness ahead of them was darker than that around them.

Mary managed a wobbly smile. "Just wait here a minute while I check it out," Joseph murmured. With a flaming torch in one hand and a stout rod in the other, he entered the cave.

The stale smell of animal dung and old straw met his nostrils. Turning slowly, he shone the feeble light of the torch into the far corners of the cave. He watched tensely for the shining eyes of some lurking animal, but saw none.

Along one wall Joseph spotted something that made him smile. Herdsmen had carved out a manger from the limestone. It overflowed with straw, while wisps of it lay scattered about on the floor. *Right here,* thought Joseph, *is our child's first bed.*

Hurriedly he grabbed a great armful of straw and spread it on the floor. Then rushing out to Mary and gently helping her off the donkey after hobbling it, he led her into the cave.

Awkwardly he spread a mat over the soft but prickly straw, and Mary gratefully lay down. She shivered in the chilly air, and Joseph whipped off his woolen cloak and spread it over her.

Mary stared at him with wide, glistening eyes. "It's going to happen, Joseph. Almost any time now. My baby— *God's baby*—will be born!"

And later that night, while people in Bethlehem and surrounding villages still pushed and shoved, while peddlers and beggars still uttered their mournful cries, while shopkeepers figured how much they might make on the crowds, and dishonest priests in nearby Jerusalem reckoned the prices they could get for their sacrificial animals, something wonderful happened.

Baby Jesus was born.

Mary's soft lips brushed His damp head. In the circle of light from Joseph's clay oil lamp, she examined each of His tiny features. His pink mouth opened and closed, searching for food. He blinked His big, dark eyes, then squeezed them shut. Mary picked up one soft little hand, and the Baby's fingers curled around one of her own.

"I'll take care of You!" she whispered. "You're my little Jesus, my gift from God, and I love You!"

Women from the village had come to help, bringing water and kindness. Their job done, they left as quietly as they had arrived. Slowly Mary bathed her infant son while He filled the cave with His cries. "There, there," she murmured, "this will soon be over. I'll just rub Your skin with salt to keep it healthy, and wrap You tight in these strips of clean cloth I brought with me. You want to grow up straight and strong, don't You? Of course You do!"

Joseph watched and smiled. He thought he had never seen anything so beautiful as dark-haired Mary bending over her newborn Baby. But he began to wonder why God had let this special Child be born in a stable. Here, right here in front of his eyes, lay the Child God had promised centuries ago, of all His gifts the very best. Questions filled his mind.

But for the moment he was content to watch as Mary tenderly laid her child in the straw-filled manger. With one big yawn, God's little gift closed His eyes and went to sleep.

✕ ✕ ✕

"Hurry, Professor, put another tape in," the children chorused.

The old man smiled and fumbled with his machine. "Now, don't get me all flustered. Yup. Here it is. Maggie B outdid herself with this story. You ready?"

"Ready!" came the quick reply.

Soon the sounds of sheep echoed through the mansion. Stacey reached up and took hold of the old man's hand. "You're the best grandfather in the whole world," she whispered.

The professor blinked back a tear. "Thank you, Stacey. Thank you for saying that."

Leaning her head against the old man's knees, the girl waited for the story to begin.

✕ ✕ ✕

Millions of angels watched, amazed and speechless, while their Creator and Lord whimpered as an infant in a stable.

"How much He loves people!" Gabriel whispered. "Just think of our Creator, our Commander, lowering Himself to become a human being!"

"He followed the divine plan," another angel remembered, and the other angels nodded their shining heads. Even before the creation of the world God had worked out a way to save people from eternal death if they should sin. And that way was to send the Creator to earth as a human being.

Then as a human being, not God, He would have to live a sinless life. And finally He would die for every sinner—every man, woman, boy, or girl who had ever lived or ever would live on earth.

God turned to them, smiling through His sorrow. "Think

what this means for the human race!" He exclaimed. "Wipe the sadness from your faces, for this is a time of joy!

"Gabriel! Gather multitudes of angels, and wing your way toward earth. On a hillside in Bethlehem you will find some shepherds watching their sheep. These lowly shepherds may be despised by those around them, but unlike many people, they love Me and have been longing for the Saviour to come. So, go. Tell them the Saviour is born!"

Swifter than lightning Gabriel and thousands of angels obeyed. Now, at last, they could share the news of this wonderful birth. They could barely wait to see the expressions on the shepherds' faces when they told them that the One the world had waited for lay as an infant only a short distance away.

More quickly than they could think these thoughts, the angels found themselves hovering over the very hills David had once roamed as a shepherd boy. Below them sleepy sheep quietly chewed their cuds. And nearby sat a few shepherds, having finished penning up their flocks by surrounding them with thorn bushes. Now they discussed in serious tones the prophecies of Scripture.

A shepherd boy with big dark eyes observed, "Micah said that He would be born right here in Bethlehem, you know!"

"Yes, and Scripture also said that He'd come from the family of David," another added.

"You know," spoke up a voice from the shadows, "I heard about that old priest, Zechariah, and his wife, Elisabeth, who just gave birth to a boy named John. People say an angel announced the birth, and it certainly was a miracle at their age! Do you suppose that child might be the Messiah?"

"But old Zechariah prophesied," burst in the shepherd boy with the big, dark eyes, "and said the child, John, would prepare the way of the Lord. Doesn't that sound as if the Messiah is really on His way?" He jumped up and swung his staff in the air, too excited to sit still.

"Do you think that after the Messiah comes, people will treat us better?" another shepherd asked, his eyes bright in the firelight. "I get tired of the rich and the priests and everybody else looking down upon us just because we're shepherds. Do you think everybody will become wealthy when the Messiah sets up His kingdom?"

Then the shepherds fell silent, each dreaming about the Messiah promised so long ago.

Suddenly a brilliant light lit the whole hillside. The frightened sheep jumped up and crashed against their corral of thornbushes, bleating frantically. Terror-stricken, nearly blinded by the light, the shepherds fell facedown on the cold ground.

Then they heard a musical voice saying, "Don't be afraid! I bring you glad news of great joy to all people, for there is born this day in the city of David a Saviour, who is Christ the Lord!

"And this is how you will recognize Him: you will find a baby wrapped in cloths, lying in a manger."

Then suddenly the shepherds saw the whole sky filled with angels, and heard them singing praises to God. "Glory to God in the highest," the angels proclaimed, "and on earth peace among people!"

The night air rang with beautiful, silvery notes. Each blade of grass stood bathed in golden light, and the whole hillside shone with dazzling splendor. Then as suddenly as they had appeared, the angels vanished.

The shepherds stared blindly at each other in the sudden darkness. No one spoke. Each felt stunned at what had just happened. To think that angels had appeared to them, lowly shepherds, and had announced the birth of the Messiah—*to them!* Would people believe them? After all, everybody considered shepherds to be dishonest.

Forgetting about their sheep for once, they shouted, "Let's go to Bethlehem. Let's find the Child!"

Soon Mary and Joseph heard voices nearing their stable.

The couple held their breaths. Had the priests found out about their miracle Child, and come to welcome Him? Or possibly it was unfriendly prowlers—bandits perhaps.

Then some young men, hardly more than boys, stood in the cave's entrance. A few of them sported black whiskers. All of them bore the unmistakable smell of sheep.

Shepherds! Mary and Joseph thought. *Of all people who might find their way to the holy Child! They are among the lowest ranks of society. Where are the priests, the scribes, the important people of Israel? Surely others must be coming to welcome God's precious gift! Why were these shepherds the first to visit God's holy Child?*

But as they gazed into the shepherds' faces, they saw gentle expressions and honest eyes. Mary smiled a welcome, and Joseph invited them to enter.

In stumbling, halting words the shepherds told Mary and Joseph all about the angels' visit, and the wonderful words the beings had spoken. Then awkwardly, eagerly, they asked, "May we see Him?"

Proudly Mary moved aside so that they could see Jesus wrapped in cloths, lying in a manger, just as the angels had said. The clumsy shepherds knelt by the infant. "It's the Messiah!" they breathed, their faces radiant. "The Messiah has come at last!"

Mary and Joseph beamed at each other, then at the shepherds. Jesus had not been welcomed by the high, the mighty, the proud, or the rich. But He had been welcomed and worshiped by poor, humble shepherds. And His birth announcement had come straight from heaven!

✕ ✕ ✕

"Just one more story," Jason begged.

"Yes, please, Grandfather, let's have just one more story," Stacey said.

Professor Appleby smiled fondly at her. "One more story it is, then time to go home before your parents start worrying about you."

✕ ✕ ✕

Joseph awoke. Startled, troubled, he stared into the darkness. The dream! It had been so real he could still almost hear God's voice echoing off the walls in the little room.

"Mary!" he whispered.

Her eyelids fluttered. She turned her head, a mass of dark wavy hair falling across her young cheek.

"Mary!" he whispered again, more urgently. Gently, he shook her shoulder. Her eyes flew open, and she sat up straight.

"What? What's wrong, Joseph?"

"I've had a dream! God spoke to me and told me to take you and Jesus to Egypt because King Herod plans to kill Him!"

A little cry escaped her lips. "Then we must go. Now!"

Joseph hesitated for only a moment. He well knew the dangers and difficulties of traveling at night. But he also realized that God would protect them.

Hurriedly they packed their few belongings onto their donkey's back. And before dawn broke or a rooster crowed, Mary, Joseph, and Jesus silently slipped out of Bethlehem and away from the murderous king.

A few miles away in Jerusalem Herod was up early that morning. In fact, he had lain awake most of the night. He was sick and in pain. His body oozed an odor so dreadful that he could hardly stand himself.

Visions of his dead wife Mariamne tortured him. He had loved her above all his other wives. But he had ordered her death, convinced against all reason that she was involved in a plot to overthrow him.

In his sickness he saw threats on every hand. One by one, and hundreds by hundreds, he eliminated them. He had killed sons, soldiers, citizens, servants. And he had murdered Mariamne.

The Jews hated him—that he knew. They did not consider him one of them. After all, his ancestors had been ancient enemies of the Jews before one of them had converted to the Jewish religion. Without a doubt the Jews would seize any opportunity to do away with him. Even now he suspected their proud leaders of hatching a plot with those Wise Men from the East who had stopped to see him. "They know more than they're telling!" he whispered savagely.

Impatiently he waited for the Wise Men to return as they had promised. He would find out from them where this new "king" they asked about had been born. Then he would send soldiers to kill Him, and that would be that.

But the morning wore on, and the Wise Men didn't return. They should have been back by now—Bethlehem wasn't far away. Herod cursed and raved, throwing the palace into a frenzy of fear. The sun climbed high in the sky. Furious, frustrated, Herod screamed, "I've been tricked! They're not coming back!

"Marcus!" he shouted, and an officer stood before him. "Alert the soldiers, then carry out my orders exactly. Search out every baby boy in Bethlehem under the age of 2 and kill him. See that none escapes!"

The officer hurried to obey, a sick feeling in his stomach. He had done some terrible things in his career, but killing babies? This was the worst yet.

Herod sank back against silk pillows, a faint smile lighting his ashen face.

But while mothers in Bethlehem sobbed out their sorrow for their slaughtered sons, Mary, Joseph, and Jesus journeyed farther and farther away.

As they hurried along the couple talked quietly, praising God again and again for the honor that had come to them and for His protection.

At last, far from Bethlehem, close to the Great Sea, they picked up the much-traveled caravan route between Judea and Egypt. The donkey clip-clopped its patient way. Mary swayed gently on its back. Joseph walked along beside, guiding the animal. And Jesus slept soundly, rocked in His mother's arms.

Days passed. Each time they came to a little village or a scattering of tents, people would step out to greet them, offering food and shelter. And the gold and precious spices the Wise Men had given Jesus bought more food. Because of these gifts, the donkey's saddlebags always bulged with lentils, chickpeas, beans, dates, figs, onions, garlic, and other vegetables. Not once did they go hungry.

Finally they crossed a wadi called the "River of Egypt." Mary smiled at the grand name for the empty streambed marking an ancient boundary between Egypt and Israel. Joseph smiled for another reason. At last they could be sure they were beyond Herod's grasp.

The sun grew ever hotter as they crossed Sinai. The baby cried as dry, hot gusts of wind suddenly swept great clouds of dust into the air, blotting out the sky. Mary drew her headcloth across her face and bent low over little Jesus, protecting Him with her body.

The donkey hung its head, closing its eyes with their long lashes against the stinging sand. Joseph buried his face in the donkey's side, wrapping his arms around Mary and the Baby. At last the storm passed, but dust and grit now covered everything.

At suppertime Mary dug into the saddlebags. As best she could, she shook the dirt out of the bags of beans and lentils, and scraped it off the fruit and vegetables. But the stew that night was unusually gritty, and Joseph and Mary smiled feebly at each other as they ground sand between their teeth.

They continued southward, finally coming to a caravan fortress that seemed to specialize in selling camels. A man with a face like a piece of smiling leather approached Joseph. "Ah, friend, don't you need a camel for your journey?" He cast a scornful glance at Joseph's donkey. "I have fine camels. They will take you far and get you there quickly. They can go for days without water and will eat almost anything."

Joseph frowned. His donkey was his prize possession. And it had served him faithfully. Still, a camel could travel more easily over the desert sand.

The trader saw Joseph's hesitation. He picked up the big, round foot of the nearest camel. "Look. See those soft pads on the bottom of the feet? They are made for this country. Now, your donkey can travel well over stony ground and is all right where you come from, but not here.

"What do you say? I offer you a bargain, only eight ounces of gold."

Joseph drew back in mock surprise. "That much? Surely you are a wise man. I will give you my donkey for your camel. It is young and strong."

"Ha!" shouted the trader. "You are right, but don't you agree my camel would be insulted by such a trade?" All the while he was thinking, *I know someone who will soon be traveling north. He will need a fine donkey such as this, and I should be able to turn a handy profit.*

Joseph shrugged. "Fine. We will ride our humble beast then." And he started to walk away.

"Now, don't be hasty!" protested the trader, dashing after him, just as Joseph had known he would. "You can have the camel for your donkey and just two ounces of gold. And you are cleverly robbing me!"

"Two ounces of gold!" Joseph exclaimed. "I'll give you the donkey plus one ounce of finest myrrh. Now won't your friends envy you for such a deal?"

The trader's eyes glittered. "Five ounces!" he countered.

"Two!"

"Four!" the trader insisted.

"Two is my final offer," Joseph snapped.

"But for such a fine camel!" the trader whined, trying to figure out if Joseph really meant that was his final offer.

"Surely you can give me three ounces."

Joseph looked at the man, at the camel, then at his patient little donkey. "Two. Take it or leave it."

"Ah, you drive a hard bargain," sighed the trader, secretly pleased.

Joseph was just as pleased with the trade. The camel, a lovely buff color, knelt in the dust for Mary to climb onto its back.

Now they moved swiftly into the heart of Egypt, at last sighting the blue Nile, shining and peaceful. They marveled again and again at the green strips of fertile land on either side of the river, then at the sudden change to barren desert. And they were staggered, just as another Joseph had been centuries before, when they first caught sight of the massive pyramids.

At every turn they saw something to astonish them—the

temples to strange Egyptian gods or a hippopotamus basking in the sun. Great waterwheels pulled by oxen lifted water from the Nile to the canals, and from the canals to the fields. And the green flash of a bird called the bee-eater brought forth exclamations of delight.

But they were most pleased when they found other Jews living in Egypt. Soon they found a home near them, and settled into a peaceful, happy life.

Jesus grew round and rosy. Mary prayed every day that she would be a good mother. And every day she whispered in His little ear, "God has watched over us and guided us all the way down here to Egypt. He has protected You from wicked King Herod. Now we will just wait for Him to tell us when to go back home again."

Finally, after long months of waiting, her husband dreamed once again. "Joseph," God said, "it is safe to return to Israel now, for King Herod, who wanted to kill the Child, is dead."

And so the journey homeward began. At last they reached Israel, and Joseph turned the head of his new donkey toward Galilee. After so long a time, they finally gazed once more upon the green hills of home. And looking up into the blue sky, they whispered, "Thank You!"

✗ ✗ ✗

The later afternoon autumn sunlight slanted across the children as they started across the yard for home. Professor Appleby waved goodbye to them from the porch. Half way across the yard, Stacey glanced over her shoulder at him. Suddenly she paused, then turned and raced back to the porch. Throwing her arms around the professor, she said, "I love you, Grandfather."

SQUARE OFF

The letters in each square are located in one of nine positions: top left, top center, top right, left center, center, right center, lottom left, bottom center, and bottom right. Can you locate a three-by-three group of nine squares containing one letter in each position? When you find this block, unscramble the letters to spell the name of a very important place.

__ __ __ __ __ __ __ __

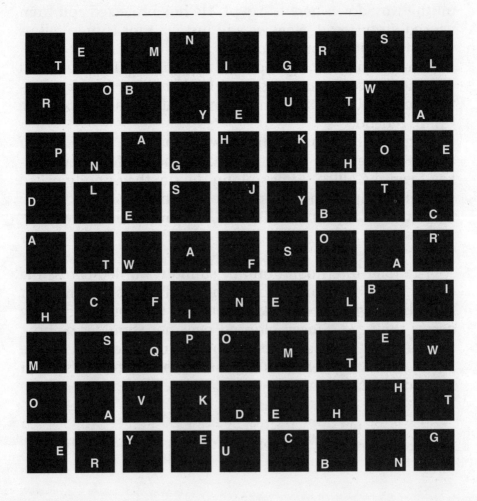

Egypt in the Time of Jesus

By the time of Jesus, Egypt had lost its ancient independence and had been controlled by foreign powers for many centuries. First the Persians, then the Greeks—under Alexander the Great—had conquered it. After the death of Alexander the Great, one of his generals, Ptolemy, set himself up as king of Egypt. His descendants ruled Egypt until the death of the famous Cleopatra in 30 B.C. Emperor Augustus then took personal control of the country for Rome, and Egypt remained almost the private possession of the emperor for a long time.

Under the Romans Egypt became the empire's breadbasket. Vast fleets of ships carried grain to feed the huge population of the city of Rome and Italy. They could not have survived without the vast amounts of food grown in the irrigated fields along the Nile. The apostle Paul may have ridden on some of those grain ships during his travels.

People from all over the ancient world came to Egypt to buy and sell and live. Greeks settled in special cities like the port city of Alexandria and controlled much of the wealth. Jews also flocked to the country. The largest community of Jews outside of Palestine lived in Alexandria. Many Jews had fled to Egypt for safety in the past. When, for example, Ishmael, son of Nethaniah, killed Gedaliah, the governor appointed by the Babylonians, he and many others fled to Egypt (2 Kings 25:25, 26). Jewish soldiers were stationed on Elephantine Island on the southern border of Egypt where they had a temple. Another Jewish temple existed at Leontopolis from 163 B.C. to A.D. 73.

Because there were so many Jews already in Egypt, it was natural for Jesus' parents to seek refuge there while Herod tried to hunt down the newlyborn Messiah. There Joseph could sell the gold and incense the Magi had given them, and find work to support his family until they could return home.

ANSWER KEYS FOR PUZZLES

PUZZLE 1: HIDDEN MEANINGS

V W P	I O L	S R A	I K N	A I N	N N I
G P P	R R H	A A A	I Y R	N I O	L N H
J **D** P	A **R** O	C **E** T	O **A** I	B **M** P	R **S** H

PUZZLE 2: JERICHO JUMBLE

PUZZLE 3: STEP BY STEP

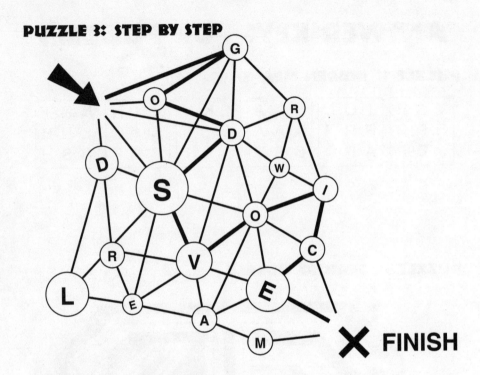

✗ FINISH

PUZZLE 4: SQUARE OFF

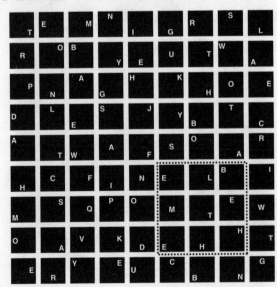

BIBLE PLACES

```
U  A  I  R  I  J  Y  X  C  M  M  V
R  F  D  A  U  E  H  S  O  D  O  M
Q  J  A  O  L  R  N  E  Y  Y  G  C
Z  G  G  Z  N  I  H  B  O  W  Q  Y
S  G  R  V  W  C  C  E  H  C  O  J
H  I  E  A  P  H  G  N  Z  X  E  B
I  B  G  Z  D  O  U  E  B  X  F  J
L  E  Y  P  J  R  F  Z  A  E  K  Y
O  O  P  I  T  I  A  E  O  R  I  V
H  N  T  K  H  U  Y  R  M  M  R  J
G  O  M  O  R  R  A  H  V  A  G  Z
I  R  T  F  R  G  N  L  P  M  R  P
```

BIBLE PEOPLE

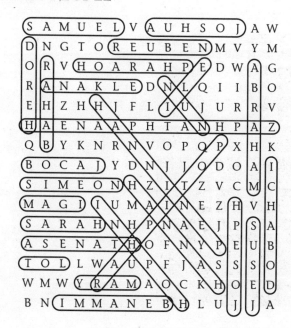

```
S  A  M  U  E  L  V  A  U  H  S  O  J  A  W
D  N  G  T  O  R  E  U  B  E  N  M  V  Y  M
O  R  V  H  O  A  R  A  H  P  E  D  W  A  G
R  A  N  A  K  L  E  D  N  L  Q  I  I  B  O
E  H  Z  H  H  F  L  I  U  J  U  R  R  V
H  A  E  N  A  P  H  T  A  N  H  P  A  Z
Q  B  Y  K  N  R  N  V  O  P  Q  P  X  H  K
B  O  C  A  J  Y  D  N  J  J  O  D  O  A  I
S  I  M  E  O  N  H  Z  I  T  Z  V  C  M  C
M  A  G  I  I  U  M  A  I  N  E  Z  H  V  H
S  A  R  A  H  N  H  P  N  A  E  J  P  S  A
A  S  E  N  A  T  H  O  F  N  Y  P  E  U  B
T  O  L  L  W  A  U  P  F  J  A  S  S  S  O
W  M  W  Y  R  A  M  A  O  C  K  H  O  E  D
B  N  I  M  M  A  N  E  B  H  L  U  J  J  A
```

The Shadow Creek Ranch Series

by Charles Mills

1. *Escape to Shadow Creek Ranch*

Joey runs through New York City's streets with a deadly secret in his pocket. It's the beginning of an escape that introduces him to a loving God, a big family, and a great new home nestled in Montana's mountains. Join him for high adventure!

2. *Mystery in the Attic*

Something's hidden in the attic. Wendy insists it's a curse. Join the kids at the ranch as they face a mystery so intense it seems to place their very lives in peril, but ultimately reveals a wonderful secret about God's power.

3. *Secret of Squaw Rock*

Summer has come to the ranch, and with it a small group of young guests, each with a past to escape and a future to discover. Share in the exciting events that bring changes to their troubled lives.

4. *Treasure of the Merrilee*

Wendy isn't talking about what she's uncovered up in the mountains, and Joey is nowhere to be found! Book 4 takes you deep into the hearts and minds of two of your favorite characters and gives you a front-row seat to events destined to change their lives forever.

5. *Whispers in the Wind*

Through the eyes of your friends at the ranch, experience the worst storm in Montana's history and a Power stronger than the fiercest winds, more lasting than the darkest night.

Each paperback US$5.95, Cdn$8.35.
Look for more books in the series coming soon.
